Philip Allan
Publishers

GCSE

Exam
Success
Guide

Mathematics
Foundation &
Intermediate Level

David Owen

Titles available

GCSE

Biology
Chemistry
French
Geography
IT and Computing
Mathematics: Foundation & Intermediate Level
Mathematics: Higher Level
Religious Studies: Christianity
Science
20th Century World History

Philip Allan Publishers Limited
Market Place
Deddington
Oxfordshire OX15 0SE

Telephone: 01869 338652

© Philip Allan Publishers Limited

Formerly published by Richard Ball Publishing
Revised 1998

ISBN 0 86003 309 0

This is a revised edition of *GCSE Mathematics: Foundation & Intermediate Level* published by Richard Ball Publishing in 1996.

Typeset by MHL Typesetting Limited, Coventry and printed by Information Press, Eynsham, Oxford

ontents

Introduction

Acknowledgements

I must thank my colleague Bill Rigby for his constructive criticisms and his suggestions of alterations. I must also thank my son, Gareth, for his proof reading and for his knowledge of 'Latex Format'. I fear that eventually he will seek payment.

Introduction

The national curriculum for Mathematics makes much reference to (a) key stages, (b) attainment targets, (c) level of attainment and (d) grades. It is the level of attainment and the grade which matter to you.

In Year 9 you were awarded a level of attainment. Most people scored from 4 to 8. The lowest is 4 and the highest is 10. However, when you are examined at 16 you will be awarded a grade instead. (Don't ask me why!) These grades range from G at the lowest end of the spectrum to A* at the highest. The examination groups examine at three tiers:

Tier	Target level	Grades awarded
Foundation	(3), 4, 5 and 6	G, F, E and D
Intermediate	5, 6, 7 and 8	G, F, E, D, C and B
Higher	7, 8, 9 and 10	D, C, B, A and A*

Your teacher may refer to A and A* topics as 'Further Material'.

If you enter a tier which is too high for you, you could get no grade at all. Your class teacher's estimate can help you to decide. If it is considered likely that you will achieve a G or F grade, then you should tackle 'Foundation'. If it is E, D or C, take 'Intermediate'. Only tackle the highest tier if you are assessed as B or better.

Some Realistic Advice

As you are studying this book you are probably following the intermediate course. Your class teacher will in all likelihood have estimated your grade as C or lower. Your clear target must be a C. It is the lowest grade respected by colleges and by many employers.

When revising, make sure you are totally at ease with all level 5, 6 and 7 topics before panicking over topics defined as Level 8. However, if your teacher thinks that you are capable of achieving a Grade B, then you can certainly improve your chances by thoroughly revising the following topics: (a) the nth term (Chapter 1); (b) inequations (Chapter 5); (c) simultaneous equations (Chapter 9); (d) all of Chapter 17; and (e) cumulative frequency curves (Chapter 22).

If you need further revision questions, then the best source by a mile is recent GCSE examination papers. Your teacher has copies of some of them. If you are desperate to get hold of your own copies, write to your examination group. It will sell you copies of the papers which have been set in the last two or three years. Avoid papers dated prior to 1994 as there have been large changes in the syllabus since then.

Number

Essential Skills

(a) A working vocabulary of words used to describe integers (whole numbers) such as odd, even, prime, square, cube, etc.

(b) A basic knowledge of indices would help, e.g. $2 \times 2 \times 2$ can be written as 2^3.

Basic Facts

The order in which calculations should be carried out is represented by BODMAS.

The method of differences helps to find further terms in number patterns and can lead to the nth term.

Standard form will be met, e.g. $170\,000 = 1.7 \times 10^5$ and $0.004 = 4 \times 10^{-3}$.

H.C.F.s and L.C.M.s will be defined.

BODMAS

When the order in which calculations are to be carried out is not clear then the agreed order is

B   Brackets are done first
O   Of is next
D   Dividing is third
M   Multiplying follows
A   Add now
S   Subtract finally

EXAMPLES 1–4

These examples should make this clearer.

Work out:

1   $5 + 8 \times 2$ M before A
    $5 + 16 = 21$

2   $(5 + 8) \times 2$ B before M
    $13 \times 2 = 26$

3   $\frac{30}{5} - 5$ D before S
    $6 - 5 = 1$

4   $\frac{(30-5)}{5}$ B before D
    $\frac{25}{5} = 5$

Try these:

1 $4 + 4 \times 6$.
2 $(4 + 4) \times 6$.
3 $\frac{20}{4} + 10$.
4 $\frac{(20+10)}{4}$.

5 $10 + \frac{1}{2}$ of 10.
6 $30 - 10 \times 3$.
7 $(30 - 10) \times 3$.

Patterns of numbers

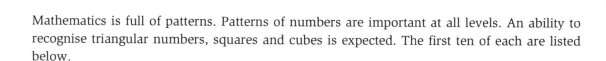

Mathematics is full of patterns. Patterns of numbers are important at all levels. An ability to recognise triangular numbers, squares and cubes is expected. The first ten of each are listed below.

Triangular	Square	Cube
1	1	1
3	4	8
6	9	27
10	16	64
15	25	125
21	36	216
28	49	343
36	64	512
45	81	729
55	100	1000

These diagrams explain where they get their names from:

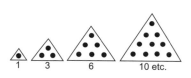

1 cm cube or 1 cm^3

2 cm cube or 8 cm^3

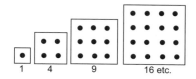

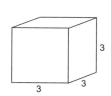

3 cm cube or 27 cm^3

You will be expected to study a sequence of numbers and be able to state the next number. You may be asked to explain the rule you used to find it.

EXAMPLES

5–12

In each example, find the fifth number, and explain your method briefly.

(5.) 7, 9, 11, 13, x $x = 15$ ✓ (2 is being added).
(6.) 5, 10, 20, 40, x $x = 80$ (they are being doubled).
(7.) 4, 8, 13, 19, y $y = 26$ (the three differences are 4, 5 and 6; the fourth difference is 7).
(8.) 25, 36, 49, 64, y $y = 81$ (they are square numbers).
(9) 37, 34, 31, 28, z $z = 25$ (3 is being taken away).
(10.) 1, 3, 6, 10, a $a = 15$ (triangular numbers).
(11.) 256, 128, 64, 32, b $b = 16$ (the numbers are being halved).
(12.) 729, 512, 343, 216, c $c = 125$ (these are cubes: 9^3, 8^3, 7^3, 6^3).

EXERCISE

B

Try these:

(1) 20, 27, 34, 41,   a. add 7
(2) 45, 36, 28, 21,   b. Subtracting in descending order
(3) 1, 3, 9, 27,   c. square of circle
(4) 73, 64, 55, 46,   d. take away 9
(5) 10, 17, 26, 37,   e. n + 2
(6) $\frac{1}{8}$, $\frac{1}{4}$, $\frac{3}{8}$, $\frac{1}{2}$,   f.
(7) 8, 27, 64, 125,   g. 216 cube no.
(8) 10 000, 1000, 100, 10,   h. dropping by power of 10

The method of differences

EXAMPLE

13

Some series have no obvious pattern. The method of differences *sometimes* makes things clear.

Find the values of a and b in the sequence 3, 9, 19, 33, 51, a, b.

The first differences are 6, 10, 14 and 18, i.e. $9-3 = 6$, $19-9 = 10$, $33-19 = 14$, $51-33 = 18$.

The second differences are 4, 4 and 4, i.e. $10-6$, $14-10$, $18-14$.

Set the work out like this:

	3		9		19		33		51		a		b
1st difference:		6		10		14		18		x		y	
2nd difference:			4		4		4		($\therefore$ 4, 4 — a clear pattern here)					

$$\therefore x = 22 \text{ and } y = 26$$
$$\therefore a = 73 \text{ and } b = 99.$$

EXAMPLE

14

It sometimes takes three differences:

Find a and b of the sequence 4, 18, 56, 130, 252, a, b.

	4		18		56		130		252		a		b
1st difference:		14		38		74		122		x		y	
2nd difference:			24		36		48		p		q		
3rd difference:				12		12			($\therefore$ 12, 12)				

$$\therefore p = 60 \quad \text{and} \quad q = 72$$
$$\therefore x = 182 \quad \text{and} \quad y = 254.$$
$$\text{Finally, } a = 434 \text{ and } b = 688.$$

EXERCISE

C

Try these. Some are very easy and one difference is enough. Some need two differences. The hardest need three. Find the next two numbers.

1 7, 10, 13, 16, 19. **5** 0, 12, 32, 60, 96.

2 10, 17, 24, 31, 38. **6** 1, 8, 27, 64, 125.

3 2, 8, 18, 32, 50. **7** 1, 22, 79, 190, 373.

4 2, 11, 26, 47, 74. **8** 6, 21, 46, 81, 126.

The nth term

This topic is at its most difficult when the nth term is requested. The method of differences is a great help. If you are lucky it will be a '1 difference pattern'.

EXAMPLES

15–16

Consider these patterns:

15 7, 10, 13, 16; **16** 3, 9, 15, 21.

(a) State the fifth number in each pattern.

(b) Explain in words the rule to find the nth term when n is any number.

(c) Explain the algebraic formula for the nth term.

15	n	1	2	3	4
	pattern	7	10	13	16
	1st difference		3	3	3

This is the three times table slightly disguised. The formula for the three times table is $3n$. You must pull this out of the air.

Compare our pattern with the three times table:

table	3	6	9	12
our pattern	7	10	13	16

(a)   Clearly the fifth term is 19.
(b)   Multiply the term number by 3 and add 4.
(c) $3n + 4$.

16	n	1	2	3	4
	pattern	3	9	15	21
	1st difference		6	6	6

This is only the six times table adjusted. You must think of $6n$ immediately.

table	6	12	18	24
our table	3	9	15	21

(a)   The fifth term is 27.
(b)   You multiply the term number by 6 then take 3 away.
(c) $6n - 3$.

Try these:

1   5, 9, 13, 17.
2   4, 11, 18, 25.
3   7, 9, 11, 13.
4   3, 8, 13, 18.

A two difference pattern

Sometimes the pattern takes two differences. Consider the square numbers:

	1		4		9		16		25		36
1st difference		3		5		7		9		11	
2nd difference			2		2		2		2		

You have to know that if a pattern takes two differences then the examiner has 'fiddled' with square numbers.

Find the nth terms of:

17   3, 6, 11, 18, 27;   **18**   3, 12, 27, 48, 75.

17	Our pattern	3		6		11		18		27
	1st difference		3		5		7		9	
	2nd difference			2		2		2		

It took two differences. The formula contains n^2.

n	1	2	3	4	5	
n^2	1	4	9	16	25	
our pattern	3	6	11	18	27	$(+2)$

By inspection the nth term is $n^2 + 2$.

18	our pattern	3		12		27		48		75
	1st difference		9		15		21		27	
	2nd difference			6		6		6		

It took two differences.

n	1	2	3	4	5	
n^2	1	4	9	16	25	
our pattern	3	12	27	48	75	$(\times 3)$

The nth term is $n^2 \times 3 = 3n^2$.

EXERCISE

E

Find the nth term of these:

(a) 0, 3, 8, 15, 24;

(b) 2, 8, 18, 32, 50;

(c) 11, 14, 19, 26, 35.

Patterns with fractions

Sometimes the pattern is one of **fractions**, e.g. $\frac{2}{5}, \frac{4}{8}, \frac{6}{11}, \frac{8}{14}$.

Treat the numerator and the denominator separately:

e.g.   numerator   2   4   6   8 $\therefore$ nth term is $2n$
      denominator   5   8   11   14 $\therefore$ nth term is $3n + 2$

So the nth fraction is $\dfrac{2n}{3n + 2}$.

EXERCISE

F

Find the nth term of:

(a) 9, 15, 21, 27;

(b) 6, 13, 20, 27;

(c) 6, 9, 14, 21;

(d) 2, 6, 12, 20;

(e) $\frac{1}{3}, \frac{2}{5}, \frac{3}{7}, \frac{4}{9}$;

(f) $\frac{1}{3}, \frac{3}{6}, \frac{5}{9}, \frac{7}{12}$.

Directed numbers

Directed numbers occur occasionally in our number work. Examples include temperature, current accounts at banks, and BC and AD problems.

This table records six different temperatures at times on a certain winter day.

Time	01.00h	05.00h	09.00h	13.00h	17.00h	21.00h
Temperature	$-5°C$	$-11°C$	$-3°C$	$+5°C$	$+4°C$	$-1°C$

Calculate the changes of temperature between (a) 01.00h and 05.00h, (b) 05.00h and 09.00h, (c) 09.00h and 13.00h, (d) 13.00h and 17.00h and (e) 17.00h and 21.00h.

(a) $(-11) - (-5) = -11 + 5 = -6$ (it fell 6°C)
(b) $-3 - (-11) = -3 + 11 = 8$ (it rose 8°C)
(c) $(5) - (-3) = 5 + 3 = 8$ (it rose 8°C)
(d) $4 - (+5) = -1$ (it fell 1°C)
(e) $-1 - (+4) = -1 - 4 = -5$ (down 5°C).

When money is kept in a current account at a bank it is possible for the account to be overdrawn. That means that you can have less than nothing in your account! Here is an example of a bank statement.

Type of transaction	Balance	
Opening balance	$+£\,9$	Notice that deposits are added, and
Cheque £10	$-£\,1$	cheques and withdrawals are subtracted.
Deposit £20	$+£19$	
Cash withdrawal £30	$-£11$	

20 The balance of an account is $-£30$. A deposit of £100 is made. What is the new balance?

$-£30 + £100 = £70.$

21 A cheque for £50 is drawn on an account of balance £10. What is the new balance?

$£10 - £50 = -£40.$

22 After a cash withdrawal of £40 the balance of an account stood at $-£55$. Find the previous balance.

$-£55 + £40 = -£15.$

Occasionally, in history BC and AD dates are compared.

23   A man born in 60 BC died in AD 10. How old was he when he died?

$10 - (-60) = 70$.

24   If a woman's fiftieth birthday fell in AD 25. In which year was she born?

$25 - 50 = -25$, so she was born in 25 BC.

25   A pot made in 1100 BC was found 3000 years later. In which year was it discovered?

$3000 - 1100 = 1900$. It was discovered in AD 1900.

EXERCISE

G

1   Five temperatures were recorded one morning. This table gives the readings and the times they were taken.

Time	01.00h	03.00h	05.00h	07.00h	09.00h
Temperature	$-4°C$	$-9°C$	$-11°C$	$-8°C$	$+1°C$

Find the changes between (a) 01.00h and 03.00h, (b) 03.00h and 05.00h, (c) 05.00h and 07.00h, (d) 07.00h and 09.00h.

2   A student's bank balance was $+£45$. She withdrew £78. What was her new balance?

3   Alexander the Great was born in 356 BC. What year was exactly 1000 years later?

The standard form of a number

Large numbers are often written in standard form
e.g. $2\,000\,000 = 2 \times 10^6$, $170\,000 = 1.7 \times 10^5$.

Notice that the 2 and the 1.7 are between 1 and 10 and the 6 and 5 are whole numbers.
So $14\,500\,000 = 1.45 \times 10^7$ and $25\,000 = 2.5 \times 10^4$.

Very small numbers can be written in a similar way using a negative index
e.g. $0.000\,41 = 4.1 \div 10^4$ but is written as 4.1×10^{-4} and $0.003 = 3 \times 10^{-3}$.

It may help you to spot that the number of noughts in these small quantities is the same as the negative index. In the last example 0.003 has three zeros . The index is -3.

Write these numbers in standard form: (a) 5000, (b) 16 000, (c) 1 800 000, (d) 17 800 000, (e) 0.18, (f) 0.0245, (g) 0.005, (h) 0.000 014.

You will be expected to reverse this skill.

EXAMPLE

26

What numbers are represented by

(a) 1.4×10^3?   This is $1.4 \times 1000 = 1400$.
(b) 1.85×10^5? $1.85 \times 100\,000 = 185\,000$.
(c) 8×10^{-2}? $8 \div 100 = 0.08$.
(d) 3.75×10^{-5}? $3.75 \div 100\,000 = 0.000\,037\,5$.

Write as numbers (a) 1.8×10^3, (b) 1.25×10^7, (c) 2×10^{-4}, (d) 7.5×10^{-2}.

The EXP key

On a few calculators this key may be labelled EE.

You will be expected to carry out calculations with numbers given in standard form. The EXP key is invaluable here. Unfortunately students very rarely use it. I strongly recommend that you get your calculator now. Find this key, and work through these examples.

27 If $a = 4.4 \times 10^6$ and $b = 1.25 \times 10^5$ find the value of $a \times b$ (usually written ab). Leave your answer in standard form. In these solutions EXP means press that key and $\pm$ means press the 'change sign' key.

Simply type 4.4 EXP 6 $\times$ 1.25 EXP 5.

There is one weakness. Most calculators leave the answer like this 5.5   big gap   11. This will not do for the examiner. You must write 5.5×10^{11}.

28 Divide 1.68×10^5 by 1.2×10^{-2}. Give the answer in standard form.

You type 1.68 EXP 5 $\div$ 1.2 EXP 2$\pm$ =, then 14 000 000 appears. This is the answer, but you will have to change it to 1.4×10^7 yourself.

In this exercise give all the answers in standard form.

1 How much greater than 4×10^6 is 1.3×10^7?
2 A large rectangle's length is 3.75×10^4m and its breadth is 1.6×10^3m. Calculate its area.

3 The population of Cheshire is 9.4×10^5. There are 1.46×10^6 people in Staffordshire. What is the total population of these two counties?

4 How many times greater than 4×10^{-6} is 2.48×10^{-2}?

Prime factors

A prime number is a number which has no factors except itself and 1;

e.g. $7 = 7 \times 1$ only;   7 is prime

$23 = 1 \times 23$ only;   23 is prime.

The primes which will occur most often in this section are 2, 3, 5, 7, 11 and 13.

Every whole number can be expressed as the product of prime numbers;

e.g. $30 = 2 \times 3 \times 5$

$31 = 1 \times 31$ (31 is prime)

$32 = 2 \times 2 \times 2 \times 2 \times 2$ (or 2^5)

$33 = 3 \times 11$

$34 = 2 \times 17$

$35 = 5 \times 7$

$36 = 2 \times 2 \times 3 \times 3$ (or $2^2 \times 3^2$)

EXAMPLE

29

Direct questions on this topic are much too easy, I'm afraid.

1 Find $2 \times 3 \times 7$ (42, of course).

2 A question like 'Find the prime factors of 42' is much more likely. For the solution, reverse the method used in **1**.

Divide 2 | 42   42 is even ($\div 2$)

3 | 21   21 is in the $3\times$ table ($\div 3$)

| 7   7 is prime.

So $42 = 2 \times 3 \times 7$.

3 Find the prime factors of 330.

2 |330   330 is even ($\div 2$)

3 |165   165 is divisible by 3 ($\div 3$)

5 | 55   55 is divisible by 5 ($\div 5$)

11   11 is prime.

Therefore $330 = 2 \times 3 \times 5 \times 11$.

4   Express 144 as a product of prime factors.

$$
\begin{array}{r|r}
2 & 144 \\
2 & 72 \\
2 & 36 \\
2 & 18 \\
2 & 9 \\
3 & 3 \\
\hline
& 3
\end{array}
$$

Therefore, $144 = 2 \times 2 \times 2 \times 2 \times 3 \times 3$ or $2^4 \times 3^2$.

EXERCISE

K

Express the following as the product of prime factors:

1   120.

2   105.

3   125.

4   770.

5   156.

When two numbers are considered at the same time, their highest common factor (H.C.F.) and lowest common multiple (L.C.M.) can be picked out.

EXAMPLES

30–31

30   Express 40 and 60 as the product of prime factors. Use your answers to find the H.C.F. and L.C.M. of these two numbers.

$$
\begin{array}{r|r}
2 & 40 \\
2 & 20 \\
2 & 10 \\
\hline
& 5
\end{array}
\qquad\qquad
\begin{array}{r|r}
2 & 60 \\
2 & 30 \\
3 & 15 \\
\hline
& 5
\end{array}
$$

Therefore $40 = \mathbf{2} \times \mathbf{2} \times 2 \times \mathbf{5}$
and $60 = \mathbf{2} \times \mathbf{2} \times 3 \times \mathbf{5}$.

The common factors are 2, 2 and 5, so the H.C.F. must be $2 \times 2 \times 5 = 20$.

The L.C.M. must contain all the factors of both.
i.e. $2 \times 2 \times 2 \times 5 \times 3 = 120$.

Therefore, the H.C.F. is 20 and the L.C.M. is 120.

31   Express 484 and 132 as the products of prime factors. Use your answers to show that:

(a) the H.C.F. is 44;

(b) 484 is a square number. State its square root.

$$
\begin{array}{r|r}
2 & 484 \\
2 & 242 \\
11 & 121 \\
\hline
& 11
\end{array}
\qquad\qquad
\begin{array}{r|r}
2 & 132 \\
2 & 66 \\
3 & 33 \\
\hline
& 11
\end{array}
$$

Therefore $484 = 2 \times 2 \times 11 \times 11$
and $132 = 2 \times 2 \times 11 \times 3$.

Exercise

Exer

Chapter 1

(a) The common factors are 2, 2 and 11.
Therefore, the H.C.F. is $2 \times 2 \times 11 = 44$.

(b) $484 = (2 \times 11) \times (2 \times 11)$
Therefore $\sqrt{484} = 2 \times 11 = 22$.

EXERCISE L

Use prime factors to find the answers to these four questions:

1 The L.C.M. of 16 and 24.
2 The H.C.F. of 90 and 135.
3 The square root of 900.
4 The cube root of 1728.

EXERCISE M

This exercise covers all the topics covered in this first chapter.

1 Calculate (a) $9 + 6 \times 4$; (b) $(9 + 6) \times 4$; (c) $10 + \frac{1}{2}$ of $(8 - 6)$; (d) $\frac{30}{2} - 30$.
2 Find the fifth term of each of these number sequences: (a) $146, 123, 102, 83$; (b) $7, 19, 31, 43$; (c) $84, 77, 70, 63$; (d) $1, 3, 6, 10$.
3 Find the values of (a) $(-6) + (-3)$; (b) $(-6) + (+3)$; (c) $(-3) + (+6)$; (d) $(+8) + (-2)$.
4 How much must I withdraw from my bank account for the balance to change from $+ \pounds 30$ to $- \pounds 20$?
5 At midnight on a certain day the temperature was $+ 2°C$. By 2 a.m. it had fallen by $5°C$ and by 4 a.m. it had fallen a further $2°C$. What were the temperatures at (a) 2 a.m. and (b) 4 a.m.?
6 Julius Caesar invaded Britain in 55 BC. St Paul died in AD 65. How many years passed between these two events?
7 Find nth term of each of these series of numbers: (a) $9, 11, 13, 15$; (b) $5, 8, 13, 20$; (c) $\frac{2}{5}, \frac{4}{7}, \frac{6}{9}, \frac{8}{11}$.
8 (a) Change 2.8×10^7 to a number; (b) write 5 million in standard form; (c) multiply 7×10^9 by 2×10^4.
9 Use prime factors to find the H.C.F. of 80 and 120.
10 Use prime factors to find the L.C.M. of 105 and 140.

Answers

ise **A** 1 28   2 48   3 15   4 7.5   5 15   6 0   7 60.

B 1 $a = 48$ 2 $b = 15$ 3 $c = 81$ 4 $d = 37$ 5 $e = 50$ 6 $f = \frac{5}{8}$ 7 $g = 216$
8 $h = 1$.

Chapter 1

Exercise C   **1** 22, 25   **2** 45, 52   **3** 72, 98   **4** 107, 146   **5** 140, 192   **6** 216, 343
              7 646, 1027   **8** 181, 246.

Exercise D   **1** $4n + 1$ **2** $7n - 3$ **3** $2n + 5$ **4** $5n - 2$.

Exercise E   **1** $n^2 - 1$ **2** $2n^2$ **3** $n^2 + 10$.

Exercise F   (a) $6n + 3$ (b) $7n - 1$ (c) $n^2 + 5$ (d) $n^2 + n$ (e) $\frac{n}{2n+1}$ (f) $\frac{2n-1}{3n}$.

Exercise G   **1** (a) $-5°C$, (b) $-2°C$, (c) $+3°C$, (d) $+9°C$ **2** $-£33$ **3** AD 644.

Exercise H   (a) 5×10^3 (b) 1.6×10^4 (c) 1.8×10^6 (d) 1.78×10^7 (e) 1.8×10^{-1}
              (f) 2.45×10^{-2} (g) 5×10^{-3} (h) 1.4×10^{-5}.

Exercise I   (a) 1800   (b) 12 500 000   (c) 0.0002   (d) 0.075.

Exercise J   **1** 9×10^6 **2** 6×10^7 **3** 2.4×10^6 **4** 6.2×10^3.

Exercise K   **1** $2^3 \times 3 \times 5$ **2** $3 \times 5 \times 7$ **3** 5^3 **4** $2 \times 5 \times 7 \times 11$ **5** $2^2 \times 3 \times 13$.

Exercise L   **1** 48   **2** 45   **3** 30   **4** 12.

Exercise M   **1** (a) 33, (b) 60, (c) 11, (d) -15 **2** (a) 76, (b) 55, (c) 56, (d) 15
              3 (a) -9, (b) -3, (c) $+3$, (d) $+6$ **4** £50   **5** (a) $-3°C$, (b) $-5°C$ **6** 120 years
              7 (a) $2n + 7$, (b) $n^2 + 4$, (c) $\frac{2n}{2n+3}$ **8** (a) 28 000 000, (b) 5×10^6, (c) 1.4×10^{14}
              9 40   **10** 420.

Chapter 2

Fractions, Percentages and Decimals

You have tackled the skills in this chapter many times. Nevertheless, they are important. They will be used over and over again in other chapters.

Essential Skills

(1) Be totally at ease with your calculator, especially the fraction key.

(2) Understand equivalence of fractions (don't panic, an explanation follows).

(3) Have a working knowledge of common decimals, e.g. $0.25 = \frac{1}{4}$ and a similar knowledge of percentages, e.g. $50\% = \frac{1}{2}$.

Basic Facts

(a) You will meet:
   (i)   repeated use of the fraction key; sometimes referred to as FK;
   (ii) the four rules of fractions ($+$, $-$, $\times$ and $\div$);
   (iii) the four rules of decimals.
(b) You will carry out % calculations, e.g. find 18% of £150.
(c) You will find out how to express one quantity as a fraction of another.
(d) The following facts will be stressed:
   (i)   1 figure decimals are tenths, e.g. $0.7 = \frac{7}{10}$;
   (ii) 2 figure decimals are hundredths, e.g. $0.19 = \frac{19}{100}$, etc.;
   (iii) a percentage is equal to a fraction of denominator 100.
(e) To change a fraction or a decimal to a percentage multiply by 100.

Section A: fractions

Fraction keys

Most scientific calculators now have a **fraction key**. On mine it looks like this: $a\frac{b}{c}$. A few class teachers do not stress its importance as only some of you have this key. This is a mistake. If your calculator does not have this key, then **buy one that does**.

EXAMPLE

1

$$\frac{4}{5} - \frac{2}{3}.$$

Simply type '4 **fraction key** 5'. A strange fraction appears, looking something like '4⌐5'. Then type $-$ 2 **fraction key** 3 $=$. The correct cancelled fraction appears.

If you are crafty, you can even get it to cancel fractions.

EXAMPLE
2

Cancel $\frac{36}{60}$.

Simply type 36 **fraction key** 60, then press $=$.

It automatically gives $\frac{36}{60}$ in its simplest form, $\frac{3}{5}$. Try it yourself.

From now on, the fraction key will be referred to as FK.

EXAMPLE
3

$3\frac{1}{2} + 1\frac{2}{3}$.

Simply type 3 FK 1 FK 2 + 1 FK 2 FK 3 $=$ and 5⌋1⌋6 appears.

You write $5\frac{1}{6}$ properly of course.

Without a calculator

Fractions mean 'pieces'. Look at $\frac{3}{4}$. The 3 is the number of pieces (called the numerator). The 4 is the size of the piece (called the denominator).

(a)  $\dfrac{8}{12}$

(b) 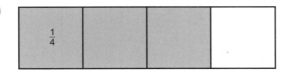 $\dfrac{2}{3}$

(c) $\dfrac{3}{4}$

(d)  $\dfrac{12}{16}$

Diagrams **(a)** and **(b)** show that $\dfrac{8}{12} = \dfrac{2}{3}$ or $\dfrac{8 \div 4}{12 \div 4} = \dfrac{2}{3}$.

Diagrams **(c)** and **(d)** show that $\dfrac{3}{4} = \dfrac{12}{16}$ or $\dfrac{3 \times 4}{4 \times 4} = \dfrac{12}{16}$.

However, we do this work without diagrams.

EXAMPLE
4

Complete these pairs of equal fractions:

(a) $\dfrac{2}{5} = \dfrac{\square}{20}$; (b) $\dfrac{3}{7} = \dfrac{\square}{14}$; (c) $\dfrac{16}{24} = \dfrac{\square}{3}$; (d) $\dfrac{21}{30} = \dfrac{\square}{10}$.

(a) $\frac{2}{5} = \frac{2 \times 4}{5 \times 4} = \frac{8}{20}$; (b) $\frac{3}{7} = \frac{3 \times 2}{7 \times 2} = \frac{6}{14}$; (c) $\frac{16}{24} = \frac{16 \div 8}{24 \div 8} = \frac{2}{3}$; (d) $\frac{21}{30} = \frac{21 \div 3}{30 \div 3} = \frac{7}{10}$.

These four examples demonstrate the idea of equal fractions (equivalence). In (c) and (d) dividing took place. This is called cancelling.

Adding and subtracting

Fractions of equal size are easy to add, e.g. $\frac{1}{4} + \frac{1}{4} + \frac{1}{4} = \frac{3}{4}$.
When the sizes are not the same, we make them so, using equivalent fractions.

EXAMPLES
5–11

5 To add $\frac{1}{2}$ and $\frac{1}{3}$, choose a common size. The best choice is $\frac{1}{6}$.

$\frac{1}{2} + \frac{1}{3} = \frac{3}{6} + \frac{2}{6} = \frac{5}{6}$.   This is usually written $\frac{3+2}{6} = \frac{5}{6}$.

6 $\frac{4}{5} + \frac{1}{3}$. The best size is $\frac{1}{15}$.

$\frac{4}{5} + \frac{1}{3} = \frac{12+5}{15} = \frac{17}{15}$.

As $\frac{15}{15}$ is one whole one, $\frac{17}{15} = 1\frac{2}{15}$.

7 Subtraction is similar: $\frac{7}{8} - \frac{1}{3}$.   Choose the size ($8 \times 3 = 24$).

$\frac{7}{8} - \frac{1}{3} = \frac{21-8}{24} = \frac{13}{24}$

A number like $3\frac{1}{2}$ is called a mixed number, partly whole (3), partly fraction ($\frac{1}{2}$). This makes questions slightly harder.

8 $3\frac{1}{2} + 1\frac{3}{7}$; $3\frac{1}{2} + 1\frac{3}{7} = 4 + \frac{7+6}{14} = 4\frac{13}{14}$.

9 $1\frac{1}{2} + 1\frac{5}{6}$; $1\frac{1}{2} + 1\frac{5}{6} = 2 + \frac{3+5}{6} = 2\frac{8}{6} = 3\frac{1}{3}$.

10 $1\frac{2}{3} - \frac{1}{5}$; $1\frac{2}{3} - \frac{1}{5} = 1 + \frac{10-3}{15} = 1\frac{7}{15}$.

Things can get a little more complicated.

11 $3\frac{1}{3} - 1\frac{9}{10} = 2 + \frac{10-27}{30}$.

We cannot take 27 from 10; one of the whole numbers must be changed to thirtieths. We then have: $1 + \frac{30+10-27}{30} = 1\frac{13}{30}$.

Multiplying

This is more straightforward.

EXAMPLES
12–17

12 $\frac{1}{3} \times \frac{4}{5} = \frac{4}{15}$.

Simply multiply the numerators, then the denominators. However, sometimes it is worth cancelling first.

13 $\dfrac{2}{\cancel{3}_1} \times \dfrac{\cancel{6}^2}{7} = \dfrac{4}{7}$.

14 $\dfrac{\cancel{27}^3}{\cancel{32}_4} \times \dfrac{\cancel{8}^1}{\cancel{45}_5} = \dfrac{3}{20}$.

Mixed numbers can be dealt with quickly:

15 $1\frac{3}{5} \times 1\frac{7}{8}$, $1\frac{3}{5} = \frac{8}{5}$ and $1\frac{7}{8} = \frac{15}{8}$

$\dfrac{8}{5}$ and $\dfrac{15}{8}$ are called improper fractions. $\dfrac{\cancel{8}^1}{\cancel{5}_1} \times \dfrac{\cancel{15}^3}{\cancel{8}_1} = \dfrac{3}{1} = 3$.

Multiplying fractions can be used in basic calculations involving the word 'of'.

16 Find $\frac{3}{4}$ of £20. The 'of' becomes $\times$.

$\dfrac{3}{\cancel{4}_1} \times \dfrac{\cancel{20}^5}{1} = \dfrac{15}{1} = £15$.

17 Find $\frac{7}{10}$ of 15 kg.

$\dfrac{7}{\cancel{10}_2} \times \dfrac{\cancel{15}^3}{1} = \dfrac{21}{2} = 10\frac{1}{2}$ kg.

Division

If a hockey team cut six oranges into quarters, they get 24 pieces: $6 \div \frac{1}{4} = 24$.

This illustrates the famous 'dodge' used when dividing fractions, i.e. 'invert and multiply'.

$6 \div \frac{1}{4} = 6 \times \frac{4}{1} = 24$.

EXAMPLES

18–21

18 $12 \div \frac{2}{3}$. $\div$ becomes $\times$, $\frac{2}{3}$ becomes $\frac{3}{2}$; $\frac{12}{1} \times \frac{3}{2} = 18$.

19 $6\frac{2}{3} \div 2\frac{1}{2}$. $\frac{20}{3} \div \frac{5}{2} = \frac{20}{3} \times \frac{2}{5} = 2\frac{2}{3}$.

The next skill is an important one and cannot be left for the calculator to do for you! We often have to express one quantity as a fraction of another.

20 What fraction of 3 m is 80 cm?

First, change both quantities to the same unit: 3 m = 300 cm.
The fraction is $\frac{80}{300}$. This cancels to $\frac{4}{15}$.
(I typed 80 **fraction key** 300 = into my calculator.)

21 Express £2.80 as a fraction of £5.

£5 = 500p and £2.80 = 280p
The fraction is $\frac{280}{500}$ or $\frac{14}{25}$ (again calculator used).

Much practice is needed with fractions. Exercises A and B follow. Attempt A now and leave B to a later date. Please note that only four of these 18 questions cannot simply be typed into your calculator. They are 1 and 8 in exercise A and 2 and 6 in exercise B. (I hope you knew that.)

EXERCISE A

1 Complete this pair of equal fractions: $\frac{4}{5} = \frac{\square}{25}$.

2 Cancel $\frac{21}{28}$.

3 Find $\frac{2}{3} + \frac{4}{5}$.

4 $3\frac{1}{2} - 1\frac{2}{5}$.

5 $3\frac{1}{3} \times \frac{6}{25}$.

6 $7\frac{1}{2} \div 1\frac{1}{4}$.

7 Find $\frac{3}{8}$ths of £40.

8 What fraction of £1.60 is £1.40?

EXERCISE B

1 Cancel $\frac{25}{30}$.

2 Complete this statement $\frac{2}{3} = \frac{14}{\square}$.

3 $1\frac{3}{8} + \frac{4}{5}$.

4 $1\frac{3}{20} - \frac{3}{4}$.

5 Find $\frac{7}{12}$ths of 18 m.

6 Express 150 g as a fraction of 2 kg.

7 $6 \div \frac{3}{4}$.

8 $6\frac{2}{5} \times 1\frac{7}{8}$.

Section B: percentages

In every question involving percentages you either (a) divide by 100 first or (b) do the very reverse of this which is to multiply by 100 last.

EXAMPLES 22–27

These six examples should illustrate this to you.

22 Change (a) 35% and (b) $62\frac{1}{2}$% to cancelled fractions.

(a) $35\% = \frac{35}{100} = \frac{7}{20}$.

(b) $62\frac{1}{2}\% = \frac{62\frac{1}{2}}{100}$, but $\frac{62\frac{1}{2}}{100} = \frac{125}{200}$ $\left(\frac{62\frac{1}{2} \times 2}{100 \times 2}\right)$

$\therefore 62\frac{1}{2}\% = \frac{5}{8}$ as $\frac{125}{200}$ FK $= \frac{5}{8}$ (It cancels!)

23 Change $\frac{19}{50}$ to a percentage.

$\frac{19}{50} \times \frac{100}{1} = 38\%$.

24 What percentage of £6 is £3.60?

Find the fraction first. The fraction, working in pence, is $\frac{360}{600} = \frac{3}{5}$.

Therefore, the percentage is $\frac{3}{5} \times \frac{100}{1} = 60\%$.

25 (a) Find 32% of £75.   (b) Find $17\frac{1}{2}\%$ of £80.

(a) First convert the percentage to a fraction.

$32\% = \frac{32}{100} = \frac{8}{25}$.

To find $\frac{8}{25}$ of £75, replace the 'of' by '×'.

$\frac{8}{25} \times \frac{75}{1} = £24$.

(b) Again, change the percentage to a fraction.

$17\frac{1}{2}\% = \frac{17\frac{1}{2}}{100} = \frac{35}{200} = \frac{7}{40}$ $\frac{7}{40} \times \frac{80}{1} = £14$.

26 The price of a fridge before V.A.T. at $17\frac{1}{2}\%$ is £160. Find the selling price of the fridge after V.A.T. is added.

$17\frac{1}{2}\% = \frac{17\frac{1}{2}}{100} = \frac{35}{200} = \frac{7}{40}$ V.A.T. is $\frac{7}{40} \times \frac{160}{1} = £28$.

The selling price is £160 + £28 = £188.

27 A man bought a car for £6000 and sold it 2 years later for £4920. Find his percentage loss.

Remember, percentage profit or loss is always calculated in terms of the cost price. The loss is £6000 − £4920 = £1080.

The fraction loss is $\frac{1080}{6000}$ or $\frac{9}{50}$.

The percentage loss is $\frac{9}{50} \times \frac{100}{1} = 18\%$.

EXERCISE C

Try these five questions.

1 Change (a) 40% and (b) $7\frac{1}{2}\%$ to cancelled fractions.

2 (a) Find 18% of £90. (b) Find $22\frac{1}{2}\%$ of 120 kg.

3 Express 900 g as a percentage of 2 kg.

4 Increase £140 by 30%.

5 A shopkeeper makes a profit of £2.50 when he sells an article for £15. Find his percentage profit.

Reverse percentages

Percentage problems in reverse often puzzle students. I suggest that you should always aim to find 1%. These three examples should make this clear.

EXAMPLES 28–30

28 35% of a number is 28. Find the number.

As 35% of the number is 28, then 1% of the number is $28 \div 35$ or $\frac{28}{35}$.

Therefore 100% of the number is $\frac{28}{35} \times \frac{100}{1} = 80$.

29 A shopkeeper sold an item for £67.50 and made a profit of 35%. Find his cost price.

It is important to realise that £67.50 is 135% of the cost price $(100 + 35)$.

135% of the cost is £67.50. 1% of the cost is $67.50 \div 135$ or $\frac{67.50}{135}$ or 50p.
100% is 50p $\times 100 = £50$.

30 A car was sold at a loss of 24% of its cost for £1900. What was its original cost?

The vital % is 76 $(100-24)$.
76% is 1900, so $1\% = 1900 \div 76 = 25$
$100\% = 25 \times 100 = £2500$.

EXERCISE D

Attempt these six questions.

1 70% of a sum of money is £56. Find the sum of money.
2 12% of a certain number is 30. What is this number?
3 A nurse received a rise of 8% per hour. He was then earning £10.26 an hour. What was his rate of pay before the rise? If your answer is about £9.44 read example **29** again!
4 The cost of a meal, including V.A.T. of $17\frac{1}{2}\%$ is £7.05. How much of the cost is the V.A.T.?
5 A house was sold at a profit of 20% for £45 000. Find its cost price.
6 Only 35% of the candidates for an exam passed. If 780 failed, how many passed?

Section C: decimals

The four rules of decimals $(+, -, \div$ and $\times)$ should be carried out on your calculator. The main skills necessary here involve changing decimals to fractions and the reverse.
You should know that

$$0.1 = \tfrac{1}{10} \qquad\qquad 0.01 = \tfrac{1}{100} \qquad\qquad \text{and } 0.001 = \tfrac{1}{1000}$$
(1 figure decimal) (2 figure decimal) (3 figure decimal)

It follows that $0.7 = \tfrac{7}{10}$, $0.19 = \tfrac{19}{100}$ and $0.143 = \tfrac{143}{1000}$, etc.

Some decimal fractions cancel when changed:

e.g. $0.4 = \frac{4}{10} = \frac{2}{5}$, $0.15 = \frac{15}{100} = \frac{3}{20}$, $0.275 = \frac{275}{1000} = \frac{11}{40}$ (FK) used for the cancelling.

You should also know that $0.5 = \frac{1}{2}$, $0.25 = \frac{1}{4}$ and $0.75 = \frac{3}{4}$.

EXERCISE

E

Change these decimals to fractions. Cancel where possible.

(a) 0.3, (b) 0.9, (c) 0.07, (d) 0.37, (e) 0.007, (f) 0.141, (g) 0.5, (h) 0.75, (i) 0.15, (j) 0.4.

Correcting to decimal places and significant figures

'Decimal places' is often written d.p.

'Significant figures' is written s.f.

Some fractions do not change to decimals readily. They recur.

$\frac{1}{3} = 1 \div 3$

Try $1 \div 3$ on your calculator.

The answer is 0.333 333 33.

$\frac{2}{3} = 2 \div 3$

$2 \div 3 = 0.666 666 66$

We rarely need more than 4 d.p., therefore

$\frac{1}{3} = 0.3333$

$\frac{2}{3} = 0.6667$.

It is the **fifth figure** (the extra figure), i.e. 0.333**3**3 and 0.666**6**6 which makes us round down in the first example (**3**3 is nearer 30 than 40) and round up in the second example (**6**6 is nearer 70 than 60).

EXAMPLE

31

31 Find (a) 0.11731 correct to 3 d.p.; (b) 0.18669 correct to 4 d.p.; (c) 0.1856 correct to 2 d.p.

(a) 0.117**3**1 = 0.117 (3 d.p.)   In all three answers the 'extra' figure is in bold.

(b) 0.1866**9** = 0.1867 (4 d.p.)

(c) 0.18**5**6 = 0.19 (2 d.p.)

Significant figures

Decimal answers are often requested to three significant figures.

EXAMPLE

32

32 Write (a) 27.418, (b) 143.9, (c) 0.5612 all correct to 3 s.f.

Significant means important.

(a) 27.418 is 27.4 (the important figures came first)

(b) 143.9   is 144   (rounding up)

(c) 0.5612 is 0.561 (the first significant figure was 5)

Notice that 4531 to 3 s.f. is 4530; to omit the nought would change the number completely.

Here is a brief exercise:

1 Write correct to 2 d.p. (a) 4.563, (b) 0.7882, (c) 9.1158.
2 Write correct to 1 d.p. (a) 11.47, (b) 9.449, (c) 0.896.
3 Write correct to 3 s.f. (a) 14.946, (b) 7.8492, (c) 7542.
4 Write correct to 2 s.f. (a) 7.849, (b) 886, (c) 0.0972.

Changing decimals to fractions

Two different methods mix well together.

EXAMPLES

33–35

33 Change these four fractions to decimals, correct to 4 d.p. where necessary:
(a) $\frac{19}{100}$; (b) $\frac{7}{8}$; (c) $\frac{3}{4}$; (d) $\frac{7}{9}$.

(a) $\frac{19}{100} = 0.19$ (within our basic knowledge);

(b) $\frac{7}{8}$ is $7 \div 8$. Using a calculator, $7 \div 8 = 0.875$;

(c) $\frac{3}{4} = 0.75$ (we know this one);

(d) $\frac{7}{9} = 7 \div 9 = 0.77777777 = 0.7778$ (4 d.p.).

(a) could have been done using $19 \div 100$ and (c) by $3 \div 4$. If in doubt, *use your calculator*.

This skill has several uses. It is used a great deal in trigonometry (see Chapter 17). It can be used to compare fractions.

34 Show that $\frac{5}{16}$ is greater than $\frac{3}{10}$.

$\frac{5}{16} = 0.3125$ (calculator used); $\frac{3}{10} = 0.3$, so clearly $\frac{5}{16}$ is greater.

35 Write these fractions in ascending order (in order of size, the smallest first) $\frac{3}{8}, \frac{7}{20}, \frac{2}{5}, \frac{4}{11}$.

$\frac{3}{8} = 0.375$ ($3 \div 8$); $\frac{7}{20} = 0.35$ ($7 \div 20$)

$\frac{2}{5} = 0.4$ etc.; $\frac{4}{11} = 0.3636$.

The order is $\frac{7}{20}, \frac{4}{11}, \frac{3}{8}, \frac{2}{5}$.

1 Change to decimals: (a) $\frac{9}{100}$; (b) $\frac{17}{40}$; (c) $\frac{3}{13}$.

2 Arrange these fractions in descending order: $\frac{2}{9}, \frac{1}{4}, \frac{13}{50}, \frac{3}{11}$.

3 Use a decimal method to show that $\frac{24}{25}$ and $\frac{19}{20}$ differ by 0.01.

Percentage/decimal conversion

This is straightforward.

$0.73 = 73\%$ ($\times 100$)
$0.125 = 12.5\%$

$$24\% = 0.24 \qquad (\div 100)$$
$$42\tfrac{1}{2}\% = 0.425 \qquad (42\tfrac{1}{2} = 42.5)$$

The four rules of decimals

Two methods are available. The obvious method is, for all four rules, **USE YOUR CALCULATOR!**

Alternatively, make use of the following rules.

Addition and subtraction

Respect place. Add tens to tens; take tenths from tenths; etc. Keep the points under each other.

36 $4.7 + 8.45 - 6.9$.

$$
\begin{array}{r}
4.7 \\
+\ \ 8.45 \\
\hline
13.15
\end{array}
\qquad
\begin{array}{r}
13.15 \\
-6.9 \\
\hline
6.25
\end{array}
$$

i.e. $4.7 + 8.45 - 6.9 = 6.25$.

Multiplying

This method is called 'counting the points.'

37 1.2×0.9.

Treat as whole numbers: $12 \times 9 = 108$.
Count the figures after the point in the question $(1 + 1 = 2)$
The answer has two figures after the point as well, so:
$1.2 \times 0.9 = 1.08$.

38 1.1×0.11 (3 places).
$11 \times 11 \ = 121$
$1.1 \times 0.11 = 0.121$ (3 places).

Does your calculator agree?

Division

39 $1.04 \div 0.4$.

The skill is to always divide by a whole number.

$$\frac{1.04}{0.4} = \frac{10.4}{4} \qquad \text{(both multiplied by 10)}$$

$$
\begin{array}{r}
2.6 \\
4\overline{)10.4}
\end{array}
$$

Therefore, $1.04 \div 0.4 = 2.6$ as well.

40 $1.728 \div 0.12$.

This is the same as $172.8 \div 12$ (both multiplied by 100 this time).

$$12\overline{)172.8}^{\;14.4}$$

Therefore, $17.28 \div 1.2 = 14.4$ also.

The various skills in this section need to be practised. Two exercises, H and I, follow.

EXERCISE

H

1   Change 0.73 (a) to a common fraction and (b) to a percentage.
2   Change 62.5% to a decimal.
3   Change $\frac{5}{11}$ to a decimal correct to 4 d.p.
4   Write in ascending order: $\frac{4}{5}$, $\frac{5}{6}$ and $\frac{3}{4}$.
5   Write 2.348 correct to (a) 2 d.p., (b) 2 s.f.
6   Use your calculator to find: (a) $4.8 + 0.48$; (b) $5.06 - 3.1$; (c) 1.4×0.6; (d) $10.2 \div 0.6$.
7   Repeat question 6 without your calculator.

EXERCISE

I

1   Change $\frac{7}{8}$ (a) to a decimal and (b) to a percentage.
2   Use a decimal method to find the difference between $\frac{17}{20}$ and 0.83.
3   Write 7.449 correct to (a) 2 d.p., (b) 1 d.p.
4   Use your calculator to find: (a) $0.3 + 0.4 \times 2$; (b) $3 \div 0.04$; (c) 9.6×0.9.
5   Repeat the questions in 4 without using your calculator.
6   Write in descending order: $\frac{3}{5}$, $\frac{11}{20}$, $\frac{7}{11}$ and $\frac{16}{25}$.

Answers

Exercise **A**   **1** $\frac{20}{25}$ **2** $\frac{3}{4}$ **3** $1\frac{7}{15}$ **4** $2\frac{1}{10}$ **5** $\frac{4}{5}$ **6** 6   **7** £15   **8** $\frac{7}{8}$.

Exercise **B**   **1** $\frac{5}{6}$ **2** $\frac{14}{21}$ **3** $2\frac{7}{40}$ **4** $\frac{2}{5}$ **5** 10.5 m   **6** $\frac{3}{40}$ **7** 8   **8** 12.

Exercise **C**   **1** (a) $\frac{2}{5}$, (b) $\frac{3}{40}$ **2** (a) £16.20, (b) 27 kg   **3** 45%   **4** £182   **5** 20%.

Exercise **D**   **1** £80   **2** 250   **3** £9.50   **4** £1.05   **5** £37 500   **6** 420.

Exercise **E**   (a) $\frac{3}{10}$ (b) $\frac{9}{10}$ (c) $\frac{7}{100}$ (d) $\frac{37}{100}$ (e) $\frac{7}{1000}$ (f) $\frac{141}{1000}$ (g) $\frac{1}{2}$ (h) $\frac{3}{4}$ (i) $\frac{3}{20}$
(j) $\frac{2}{5}$.

Exercise **F**   **1** (a) 4.56, (b) 0.79, (c) 9.12   **2** (a) 11.5, (b) 9.4, (c) 0.90   **3** (a) 14.9, (b) 7.85,
(c) 7540   **4** (a) 7.8, (b) 890, (c) 0.097.

Exercise $\boxed{\text{G}}$ **1** (a) 0.09, (b) 0.425, (c) 0.2308 (4 d.p.)   **2** The order is $\frac{3}{11}, \frac{13}{50}, \frac{1}{4}, \frac{2}{9}$ **3** $0.96 - 0.95 = 0.01$.

Exercise $\boxed{\text{H}}$ **1** (a) $\frac{73}{100}$, (b) 73%   **2** 0.625   **3** 0.4545   **4** $\frac{3}{4}, \frac{4}{5}, \frac{5}{6}$ **5** (a) 2.35, (b) 2.3   **6** (a) 5.28, (b) 1.96, (c) 0.84, (d) 17   **7** As **6** I hope!

Exercise $\boxed{\text{I}}$ **1** (a) 0.875, (b) 87.5%   **2** 0.02 or $\frac{1}{50}$ **3** (a) 7.45, (b) 7.4   **4** (a) 1.1, (b) 75, (c) 8.64   **5** As **4**   **6** $\frac{16}{25}, \frac{7}{11}, \frac{3}{5}, \frac{11}{20}$.

Chapter 3

Proportion and Ratio

Proportion

If I buy 1 lb of bananas for 45p it is clear that I would expect to pay 3 $\times$ 45p for 3 lb. Today £1 is worth \$1.68, so £8 must be worth 8 $\times$ \$1.68. 1 kg is roughly 2.2 lb, so 6 kg must be about 6 $\times$ 2.2 lb.

These are examples of proportion. They stress how easy it is if one unit is known, i.e. 1 lb's cost, £1's worth, 1 kg's equivalent.

EXAMPLES

1–3

1 12 litres of petrol cost £8.10. What would 22 litres cost?

You must say to yourself I need to know the cost of 1 litre. This solution should follow. 1 litre costs £8.10 $\div$ 12 = £0.675; 22 litres would cost 22 $\times$ £0.675 = £14.85.

2   A recipe suggests that a shepherd's pie for six people needs 2 lb 4 oz of lamb. How much lamb is needed for eight people?

You need to know the weight needed for one person and that 2 lb 4 oz is 36 oz ($2 \times 16 + 4$). One person needs $36 \div 6 = 6$ oz; eight people need $8 \times 6 = 48$ oz or 3 lb ($48 \div 16$).

3   A workman earned £52.20 for a 7 h 15 min working day. How much would he have earned at the same rate if he had worked for only 6 h 40 min?

Many many students make the same error here. They treat these times as 7.15 h and 6.4 h. There are not 100 min in 1 h!

The 15 min is $\frac{1}{4}$ or 0.25 of an hour. 40 min is $\frac{40}{60}$ or $\frac{2}{3}$ h.

So for 1 h he earned £52.20 $\div 7\frac{1}{4}$ (I used the fraction key, $\div$ 7.25 is as good). For $6\frac{2}{3}$ h he would earn £7.20 $\times 6\frac{2}{3} = $ £48.00.

EXERCISE

A

1   Eight copies of a book cost £27.20. Find the cost of 11 such books.
2   40 litres of a washing-up liquid weighs 65 kg. What would 57 litres of this liquid weigh?
3   Change (a) 28 litres to pints and (b) 40 pints to litres.
4   The total weight of 60 identical bars of chocolate is 3.84 kg. Calculate the weight of 14 such bars. Give your answer in grams.
5   A telephone call lasting 2 min 45 s costs 33p. What would a 4 min 30 s call cost at this same rate?

Ratios

EXAMPLES

4–7

4   Share £9.40 between two friends in the ratio 3:2 (: is called the ratio sign).

3:2 means 3 shares compared to 2 shares. $3 + 2 = 5$ is a very vital sum. There are 5 shares.
1 share is £9.40 $\div 5 = $ £1.88.
3 shares is £1.88 $\times 3 = $ £5.64; 2 shares is £1.88 $\times 2 = $ £3.76 (£5.64 + £3.76 = £9.40 checks).

5   Two men shared some money. One received £1250. The other £500. Express the ratio of their shares in its simplest form.

The ratio is 1250:500	Ratios cancel like fractions.
Therefore it is 125:50	Dividing both by 10.
The answer is 5:2	Dividing both by 25.

6   A rope of length 2 ft 4 in is cut into two pieces in the ratio of 2:5. Calculate the length of the shorter piece. Give your answer in (a) inches, (b) centimetres.

There are seven shares $(2+5)$. 2 ft 4 in $= 28$ in $(2 \times 12 + 4)$.
1 share is $28 \div 7 = 4$. (a) $2 \times 4 = 8$ in. (b) $8 \times 2.5 = 20$ cm.

7 In year 11 of a certain school the ratio of boys to girls is 4:5. There are 60 boys. How many pupils are there in that year?

We have been told 4 shares. 1 share is $60 \div 4 = 15$.
There are $9 \times 15 = 135$ pupils.

EXERCISE B

1 Share £186 between two sisters in the ratio of 5:1.
2 Pewter is a mixture of tin and lead in the ratio of 4:1 by weight. A pewter jug weighs 1.1 kg. Calculate the weight of tin in this jug. Give your answer in grams.
3 Express these two ratios in their simplest form: (a) £1.44 : £1.20; (b) 2 m : 750 mm.
4 It is recommended that disinfectant is diluted in the ratio of 3:100 by volume. What volume of water should be added to 48 ml of disinfectant? Give the answer in (a) millilitres (b) litres.
5 Two people share the cleaning of some offices. Mr X works 3 days. Mrs Y works 4 days. The total wage was £79.80. (a) How much does each receive? Recently they got a rise. Mr X now gets £36. (b) How much does Mrs Y get now?

Scales

A common application of proportion and ratio is a map scale. The scale is usually given using a ratio sign, e.g.

1 cm : 4 km (or 1 cm represents 4 km)

Occasionally a sample of the scale is provided.

This is the same scale:

|_____|_____| km
0   10   20

The fraction scale $\frac{1}{100\,000}$ is the most difficult to use.

EXAMPLES 8–10

8 The scale of a map is 1 cm:4 km.

(a) Find the distance on the map representing a real distance of 14 km.
(b) Find the real distance between two points if the distance on the map is 2.5 cm.

(a) 4 km is 1 cm
    14 km is $\frac{14}{4}$ cm $= 3.5$ cm.

(b) 1 cm is 4 km
    2.5 cm is $4 \times 2.5 = 10$ km.

9 This is a rough sketch of
   Wales and Birmingham.
   The scale is 1 cm:30 km.

   (a) A helicopter flew
       directly from Rhyl to
       Cardiff. How far did it fly?
   (b) Which two places on this
       map are roughly 150 km
       apart?

   (a) Using a ruler, the distance is 6.6 cm. Therefore, the real distance is 6.6 × 30 = 198 km.
   (b) 30 km is represented by 1 cm.
       150 km is represented by 5 cm.
       By trial and error, the two places are Aberystwyth and Birmingham.

10 The scale of a map is $\frac{1}{25\,000}$. The centres of two towns are 25 cm apart on this map. How far
   are they really apart?

   This is a clumsy scale, but 100 000 cm = 1 km
      (100 cm = 1 m; 1000 m = 1 km).
   Therefore, 25 000 cm = $\frac{1}{4}$ km.
   As 1 cm represents $\frac{1}{4}$ km, 25 cm represents $\frac{1}{4} \times 25 = 6\frac{1}{4}$ km.

EXERCISE

C

1 The scale of a map is 1 cm to 15 km.

   (a) What distance would be represented by 3.2 cm?
   (b) What distance would represent 66 km on the map?

2 0   50   100 km
   |—————————|—————————|

   This is a sample scale provided on a map. What distance does

   (a) 1 cm represent?
   (b) 13.5 cm represent?

3   The scale of a map is $\frac{1}{200\,000}$.

Restate this scale in the form 1 cm:x km. What distance would be represented by 6.4 cm on this map?

4   The scale of this map of the tip of Cornwall is 1 cm to 2.5 km. Use this map to estimate:

(a) the distance from Land's End to St Ives.
(b) how much further from Land's End is Hayle than Penzance?

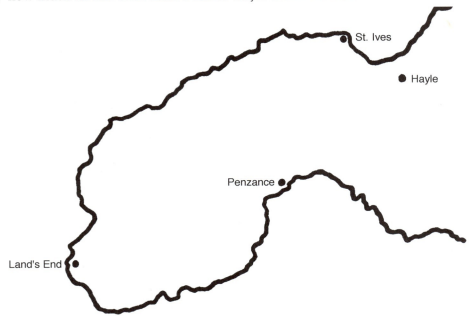

Distance, speed and time

Note that speeds can be written in three forms: (a) km.p.h, (b) km/h, (c) km h^{-1}.

Finding the distance travelled $(D = S \times T)$

EXAMPLES

11–13

11   A man walked at a steady speed of 5 m.p.h. How far did he go in 2 h?

Clearly he went $5 \times 2 = 10$ miles. The method is straightforward. Only awkward numbers or mixed units can confuse you.

12 How far will a motorist travel at 90 km/h in 2 h 20 min?

It is the 20 min which leads to errors. It is not 0.20 h! There are 60 min in 1 h. It is $\frac{20}{60}$ or $\frac{1}{3}$ of an hour.
The distance is $90 \times 2\frac{1}{3} = 210$ km (calculator used).

13 How far will an athlete run in 4 min 40 s at an average speed of 8.5 m/s. Give the answer in kilometres.

4 min 40 s = 280 s ($4 \times 60 + 40$).
The distance is $8.5 \times 280 = 2380$ m = 2.38 km ($\div 1000$).

Finding the average speed ($S = D \div T$)

AMPLES
4–16

14 I recently completed a 9 mile walk in 3 h. What was my average speed?

Speed = $9 \div 3 = 3$ m.p.h (painfully slow).
Again the method is straightforward. Only mixed units can cause confusion.

15 A runner completed a 33 km road race in 2 h 45 min. Find his average speed.

You must change the 45 min to $\frac{45}{60}$ or $\frac{3}{4}$. His speed is $33 \div 2\frac{3}{4} = 12$ km/h (fraction key used).

16 A cyclist completed a 12 km journey in 16 min. Express his speed in metres per second.

Both units must be changed. 12 km = 12 000 m (12×1000) and 16 min = 960 s (16×60).
The speed is $12\,000 \div 960 = 12.5$ m s^{-1}.

Calculating the time taken ($T = D \div S$)

AMPLES
7–19

17 How long would an 80 mile journey take at a speed of 40 m.p.h?

Time = $80 \div 40 = 2$ h.
Only fractions of hours can cause you problems.

18 The distance from Edinburgh to London is 375 miles. A high speed train can complete this journey at 100 m.p.h. How long would the journey take?

Time = 375 ÷ 100 = 3.75.   The 0.75 is not 75 min it is $\frac{75}{100}$ h or $\frac{3}{4}$ h or 45 min
= 3 h 45 min.

19 The distance between Manchester and Glasgow airports is 220 miles. If an aircraft makes this flight at 400 m.p.h. how long will the flight take?

Time = 220 ÷ 400 = 0.55 h. Do not be tempted to write 55 min. 0.55 is a decimal fraction. To change hours to minutes you multiply by 60.
Time = 0.55 × 60 = 33 min.

EXERCISE D

1 (a) Express 24 min as a fraction of an hour. (b) Change 2 min 25 s to seconds. (c) Change $3\frac{1}{2}$ h to minutes.
2 A motorist's average speed was 56 km/h. How far did she travel in 6 h?
3 A jet flight took 1 h 36 min. The jet's speed was 1200 m.p.h. Find the distance travelled.
4 A bird can fly at 12 m s⁻¹. How far will it travel in 8 min? Give your answer (a) in metres and (b) in kilometres.
5 Blackpool is 240 miles from London. A motorist completed this journey in 5 h. Calculate his average speed.
6 Marathon runners occasionally run 26 miles in 2 h 10 min. Express this speed in miles per hour.
7 A running cheetah has recorded a speed of 90 km/h. Express this speed in metres per second.
8 How long does a journey of 180 km take at an average speed of 36 km/h?
9 A motorist left Watford at 07.30 h and travelled to Newcastle-Upon-Tyne at an average speed of 54 m.p.h. The two towns are 279 miles apart. (a) How long did she take? (b) At what time did she arrive?
10 A garden snail's speed (when fully fit) has been measured at 14 mm/s. How long might the snail take to travel 2.1 m?

Answers

Exercise A   1 £37.40   2 92.6 l (3 s.f.)   3 (a) 49, (b) 231 (nearest litre)   4 896 g   5 54 p.

Exercise B   1 £155 and £31   2 880 g   3 (a) 6:5, (b) 8:3   4 (a) 1600 ml, (b) 1.6 l
5 (a) X got £34.20, Y got £45.60, (b) Y now gets £48.

Exercise C   1 (a) 48 km, (b) 4.4 cm   2 (a) 20 km, (b) 270 km   3 1 cm:2 km; 12.8 km
4 (a) about 23 km, (b) about 10 km.

Exercise D   1 (a) $\frac{2}{5}$, (b) 145 s, (c) 210 min   2 336 km   3 1920 m   4 (a) 5760 m, (b) 5.76 km
5 48 m.p.h.   6 12 m.p.h.   7 25 m s⁻¹   8 5 h   9 (a) 5 h 10 min, (b) 12.40 h
10 2 min 30 s.

Chapter 4

The Use of Letters and Substitution

Essential Skills

This first section in algebra covers many early skills. Confident students should tackle Exercise A now (at the end of this section). If weaknesses are found, return here.

Basic Facts

In algebra: **1.**   only like terms can be added

e.g. $2x + 3x = 5x$

$2x + 3y = 2x + 3y$;

2. ab is $a \times b$ $\frac{a}{b}$ is $a \div b$.

Early substitution skills will be met with letters and words:

e.g. if $a = 12$ and $b = 6$, find ab

$ab = a \times b = 12 \times 6 = 72$

or distance = speed $\times$ time. If speed is 40 m.p.h. and time is 2 h:

distance $= 40 \times 2 = 80$ miles.

Some rules of directed number will be defined, e.g. $(-5) \times (-2) = +10$.

The use of letters

We often find it useful in arithmetic to use a letter for a number, especially, of course, if that number is not yet known.

EXAMPLE

1

An unknown number plus 3 is $x + 3$.

Four times an unknown number is $4y$.

An unknown number divided by 4 is $\frac{x}{4}$.

(Note that $4 \times y$ is written $4y$ with the multiplication sign missed out, $3 \times a$ is $3a$, etc.)

Like terms

Only like terms can be added or subtracted, e.g. $4x + 5x = 9x$. (4 of *anything* and 5 of *the same thing* = 9 of them).

$5x + 2y$ cannot be written any more simply.

<table>
<tr><td>EXAMPLES
2–4</td><td></td></tr>
</table>

EXAMPLES

2–4

2   Simplify $5x + 2x + 3x$

                 $5x + 3x + 2x = 10x$ (all like terms).

3   Simplify $5y - 2y + 3x$ (collect like terms only)

                 $5y - 2y + 3x = 3y + 3x$ (no further).

4   Simplify $7y + 3x + 2y - 2x$ (1. collect ys, 2. collect xs)

                 $7y + 3x + 2y - 2x = 9y + x$ (note: $1x$ is written x).

EXERCISE

A

Try this short exercise. Simplify the following.

1   $5x + 4x - 2x$.
2   $10x - 7x - 2x$.
3   $4y + 5y + 4x$.
4   $3a + 2b + c$.
5   $5x + 3y - 2x$.
6   $7x + 4y + 4x - 4y$.
7   $5x + 3x + 2y - 6x$.

Directed numbers

These rules can be shown to be true. The rules of multiplication should be memorised.

Multiplication: $\left.\begin{array}{l}(+) \times (+) = + \\ (+) \times (-) = - \\ (-) \times (+) = - \\ (-) \times (-) = +\end{array}\right\}$ ALWAYS

Exactly the same rules hold with division.

Adding: understanding is more important than memory this time. Here is why:

$$(+) + (+) = +$$
$$(-) + (-) = -$$
$$\text{but} \quad (+) + (-) = \text{'it depends'.}$$

Here are three examples of '$(+) + (-)$' questions:

1   $(+7) + (-2) = 5$ you have 7, you owe 2, the answer is 5.
2   $(+2) + (-7) = -5$ you have only 2, you owe 7.
3   $(+2) + (-2) = 0$ of course.

Much depends on the size of the numbers. The answer depends on the sign of the larger.

Try this brief exercise.

EXERCISE

B

1   Multiply: (a) $(+4) \times (+6)$
             (b) $(+4) \times (-6)$
             (c) $(-4) \times (+6)$
             (d) $(-4) \times (-6)$.

2   Divide: (a) $(+10) \div (+2)$
             (b) $(+10) \div (-2)$
             (c) $(-10) \div (+2)$
             (d) $(-10) \div (-2)$.

3   Add: (a) $(+10) + (+4)$
             (b) $(+10) + (-6)$
             (c) $(-10) + (+6)$
             (d) $(-10) + (-6)$
             (e) $(-7) + (+7)$.

Substitution with words

Leaflets with gas bills occasionally explain how to check the bill. A 'formula' with words is provided.

EXAMPLES

5–6

5   Total bill = standing charge and number of units used × 5p.
Find the total bill if the standing charge is £3.50 and the customer uses 160 units.

By substituting, bill   = £3.50 + 160 × 5p
                    = £3.50 + £8
                    = £11.50.

6   An employee is told that the following formula will help him check his gross wages.
    Gross wage = hours worked × £3.20 + expenses.
    Find his gross wage in a week when he worked 38 h and his expenses were £4.80.

$$\text{By substituting, wages} = 38 \times 3.20 + 4.80$$
$$= 121.60 + 4.80$$
$$= £126.40 \text{ (using a calculator)}.$$

Try these four questions.

1   The perimeter of a rectangle is 2 × length + 2 × breadth.
    Find the perimeter, if the length is 14 m and the breadth 9 m.

2   The following 'formula' is used in the kitchen when cooking a chicken:
    cooking time = weight in pounds × 20 + 20.
    The answer is in minutes.
    How long does it take to cook a $4\frac{1}{2}$ lb chicken?

3   The area of a triangle is given by $\frac{1}{2}$ of base × height.
    Find the area of a triangle of base 12 cm and height 14 cm.

4   The capacity of a tank is given by length × breadth × height.
    Find its capacity if its length is 20 cm, its breadth 15 cm and its height 80 cm.

Substitution

The skill of substituting into formulae is an important one.
This practice exercise will help you in the understanding of other sections, especially Chapter 6
on Cartesian co-ordinates.

7   If $a = 3$, $b = 4$, $c = 0$ and $d = 2$, find:

(a) $ab + d$; (b) $\frac{3b}{d}$; (c) $abd + cd$.

Always substitute completely first. *Show your working.*

(a) $3 \times 4 + 2$ (using BODMAS)
    $= 12 + 2$
    $= 14.$

(b) $\frac{3\times4}{2} = \frac{12}{2}$
  $= 6.$

(c) $\quad 3 \times 4 \times 2 + 0 \times 2$
  $= 24 + 0 \qquad\qquad$ Note: $0 \times 2 = 0!$
  $= 24.$

8 $x = 8$, $y = -4$ and $z = -2$. Find:

(a) $y + z$; (b) $\frac{xy}{z}$.

(a) $(-4) + (-2) = -6.$

(b) $\frac{8\times-4}{-2} = \frac{-32}{-2} = 16 \qquad\qquad$ (as $(+) \times (-) = -$ and $(-) \div (-) = +$).

9 $x \times x$ can be written x^2 and $y \times y \times y$ can be written y^3.
   If $a = 4$ and $b = 3$ and $c = 5$, find:

(a) a^3; (b) b^2; (c) $a^2 + b^3$; (d) $2c^2$.

(a) $a^3 = 4 \times 4 \times 4 = 64.$
(b) $b^2 = 3 \times 3 = 9.$
(c) $a^2 + b^3 = 4 \times 4 + 3 \times 3 \times 3 = 16 + 27 = 43.$
(d) $2c^2 = 2 \times 5 \times 5 = 50.$

EXERCISE D

Try these four questions.

1 If $x = 8$, $y = 6$, $z = 4$ and $a = 0$, find:
   (a) $xy + za$; (b) $x + y + z + a$; (c) xyz; (d) $\frac{x}{z}$.

2 If $a = 20$, $b = 10$, $c = -5$ and $d = -2$, find:
   (a) ab; (b) $c + d$; (c) $\frac{b}{c}$; (d) ad.

3 If $x = -10$ and $y = -2$, find:
   (a) $x + y$; (b) xy; (c) $\frac{x}{y}$; (d) $x - 5y$.

4 If $x = 6$, $y = 4$ and $z = -3$, find:
   (a) $3x^2$; (b) $y^2 + z^2$; (c) $3y^3$.

Here are two miscellaneous exercises. Try E now and F later.

EXERCISE E

1 Simplify: (a) $4x + 6x - 9x$;
              (b) $3y + 2x - 3y + x$.

2 Find the values of (a) $(-7) + (-4) + (+2)$
                       (b) $(-20) \times (+2)$
                       (c) $(-15) \div (-5)$.

3   The following formula applies to solids:

    faces + vertices − 2 = edges.

    (a) How many faces has a solid with four vertices and six edges?
    (b) How many edges has a solid with six faces and eight vertices?

4   If $a = 5$, $b = 4$, $c = -3$ and $d = -2$, find:
    (a) $2a + b^2$; (b) $c + d$; (c) $ab + c$; (d) cd.

EXERCISE

1   Evaluate: (a) $(-3) + (-2) + (+4)$;
              (b) $(-10) \times (-2)$;
              (c) $-20 \div 4$.

2   Simplify: (a) $3a + 7a - 4a - a$;
              (b) $5x + 2x + 3x - 6y$.

3   If $x = 10$, $y = 6$, $b = -5$ and $d = -4$, find:
    (a) $2xy$; (b) $\frac{3x}{y}$; (c) $x + b$; (d) $x + 3b$; (e) $\frac{bd}{2}$.

4   The selling price of an article is found by using a formula:
    selling price = cost price + (cost price ÷ 4).
    Find the selling price of an item of cost price £48.

Answers

Exercise A   **1** $7x$ **2** x **3** $9y + 4x$ **4** Doesn't simplify   **5** $3x + 3y$ **6** $11x$ **7** $2x + 2y$.

Exercise B   **1** (a) 24, (b) −24, (c) −24, (d) 24   **2** (a) 5, (b) −5, (c) −5, (d) 5
3 (a) 14, (b) 4, (c) −4, (d) −16, (e) 0.

Exercise C   **1** 46 m   **2** 110 min   **3** 84 cm^2 **4** 24 000 cm^2.

Exercise D   **1** (a) 48, (b) 18, (c) 192, (d) 2   **2** (a) 200, (b) −7, (c) −2, (d) −40
3 (a) −12, (b) 20, (c) 5, (d) 0   **4** (a) 108, (b) 25, (c) 192.

Exercise E   **1** (a) x, (b) $3x$ **2** (a) −9, (b) −40, (c) 3   **3** (a) 4, (b) 12   **4** (a) 26, (b) −5, (c) 17, (d) 6.

Exercise F   **1** (a) −1, (b) 20, (c) −5   **2** (a) $5a$, (b) $10x - 6y$ **3** (a) 120, (b) 5, (c) 5, (d) −5, (e) 10
4 £60.

Chapter 5

Equations, Inequations and the Method of Trial and Improvement

Essential Skills

You need to know that

(a) if $x + 2 = 10$ then $x = 10 - 2$;

(b) if $x - 2 = 10$ then $x = 10 + 2$

(c) if $2x = 10$ then $x = \frac{10}{2}$ or $x = 10 \div 2$;

(d) if $\frac{x}{2} = 10$ then $x = 10 \times 2$;

(e) if $\frac{3x}{4} = \frac{9}{2}$ then $3x \times 2 = 4 \times 9$.

The skill (e) above is called cross multiplying and can be a great help (see Chapter 17).
You need to be able to expand brackets, e.g. $3(2x - 5) = 6x - 15$.
You will need to be able to make careful substitutions using your calculator.
$x > 10$ is read as x is greater than 10.
$x < 4$ is read as x is less than 4.
$x \geq 3$ is read as x is greater than or equal to 3.
$x \leq 5$ is read as x is less than or equal to 5.

Basic Facts

The skills above will enable you to solve equations like $5x - 3 = 18 - 2x$ and inequations like $2(4x + 5) > 50$.
You will meet inequations like $x^2 < 100$ and equations like $x^3 + 2x = 80$.

Equations

AMPLES

1–8

1   $4x + 1 = 29$ (take 1 away)

     $4x = 29 - 1$

     $4x = 28$ (divide by 4)

      $x = 7.$

2 $\quad \frac{y}{3} - 5 = 3$ $\qquad\qquad$ (add 5 on)

$\qquad \frac{y}{3} = 3 + 5$

$\qquad \frac{y}{3} = 8$ $\qquad\qquad$ (multiply by 3)

$\qquad y = 24.$

You may need to expand a bracket.

3 $\quad 4(2x + 5) = 40$ $\qquad\qquad$ (expand)

$\qquad 8x + 20 = 40$ $\qquad\qquad$ (take 20 away)

$\qquad\quad 8x = 20$ $\qquad\qquad$ ($\div 8$)

$\qquad\quad\ x = 2.5.$

The answer may be negative.

4 $\quad 4x + 3 = -9$ $\qquad\qquad$ (take 3 away)

$\qquad\quad 4x = -9 - 3$

$\qquad\quad 4x = -12$

$\qquad\quad\ x = -3.$

There may be four terms.

5 $\quad 6x - 3 = 2x + 21$

$\quad 6x - 2x = 21 + 3$

$\qquad\quad 4x = 24$

$\qquad\quad\ x = 6.$

6 $\quad 7x + 10 = 40 - 3x$

$\quad 7x + 3x = 40 - 10$

$\qquad 10x = 30$

$\qquad\quad\ x = 3.$

You may need to cross multiply.

7 $\qquad \frac{4x}{5} = \frac{11}{10}$

$\quad 4x \times 10 = 5 \times 11$

$\qquad 40x = 55$

$\qquad\quad\ x = 1.375.$

8 $\qquad \frac{5}{2x} = \frac{10}{7}$

$\quad 2x \times 10 = 5 \times 7$

$\qquad 20x = 35$

$\qquad\quad\ x = 1.75.$

Plenty of practice is essential. Here are two exercises: A and B. Do A now. Try B later.

EXERCISE A

Solve these equations.

1 $5x - 2 = 23$ $\qquad$ 2 $9x + 4 = 13$ $\qquad$ 3 $2(x + 6) = 20$ $\qquad$ 4 $4(2x + 4) = 16$

5 $\frac{x}{4} - 1 = 5$ $\qquad$ 6 $3x + 15 = -3$ $\qquad$ 7 $5x + 3 = 2x + 21$ $\qquad$ 8 $8x - 3 = 17 - 2x$

9 $\frac{3x}{4} = 9$ $\qquad$ 10 $\frac{4x}{5} = \frac{7}{2}.$

1 $6x + 1 = 25$ **2** $9x - 3 = 24$ **3** $3(3x - 2) = 30$ **4** $2(5x + 2) = 104$
5 $\frac{x}{2} + 5 = -3$ **6** $4x + 11 = 5$ **7** $7x - 2 = 5x + 12$ **8** $9x + 6 = 21 - x$
9 $\frac{2x}{3} = \frac{5}{6}$ **10** $\frac{4x}{5} = 7$.

Trial and improvement

Solutions to more difficult equations can be obtained by a method of intelligent guessing called 'trial and improvement'.

9   Find a value of x if $x^2 + x = 28$ correct to 1 d.p.

As $5^2 = 25$, $x = 5$ seems a reasonable attempt. But substituting gives:
$5^2 + 5 = 30$ (not 28) $x = 5$ is too high.
Try something less than 5, say $x = 4.7$:
$4.7^2 + 4.7 = 26.79$ too low (by 1.21).
Try $x = 4.8$:
$4.8^2 + 4.8 = 27.84$ too low (but only by 0.16).
Try $x = 4.9$:
$4.9^2 + 4.9 = 28.91$ too high (by 0.91).

∴ $x = 4.8$ is nearest to 1 d.p.
I did all these calculations on my calculator — of course!

10   Find a value of x if $x^3 - 2x = 70$ correct to 1 d.p.

Try $x = 5$: $5^3 - (2 \times 5) = 125 - 10 = 115$ much too high!
Try $x = 4$: $4^3 - (2 \times 4) = 56$ too low (but much nearer).

So try something near 4. Do not automatically try 4.5. Think!

$x = 4.2$: $(4.2)^3 - 2(4.2) = 65.688$ still too low
$x = 4.3$: $(4.3)^3 - 2(4.3) = 70.907$ too high, but much nearer than $x = 4.2$

∴ $x = 4.3$ is the answer required.

Try these four:

1   $x^2 - 2x = 45$
2   $x^2 + 3x = 100$
3   $x^3 + x = 34$
4   $x^3 - 3x = 101$.

The inequality symbols

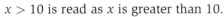

$x > 10$ is read as x is greater than 10.
$x < 10$ is read as x is less than 10.
$x \geq 5$ is read as x is greater than or equal to 5.
$x \leq 3$ is read as x is less than or equal to 3.

An integer is a whole number. The examiner may well use this word. The inequality signs are tested in the following manner.

EXAMPLES
11–13

11 x is an integer and $-1 \leq x < 3$. Make a list of the possible values of x.

In English this says that x is a whole number which could be -1 but is less than 3. The list is -1, 0, 1 and 2. Don't forget that 0 is an integer!

12 Again x is an integer and $2 < x < 7$.

The list is 3, 4, 5 and 6. Neither end is counted.

13 Finally both ends can be included.
x is an integer and $-2 \leq x \leq 2$.

Now the list is -2, -1, 0, 1 and 2.

Inequations

These resemble equations very closely. Here are some examples.
Solve these inequations:

EXAMPLES
14–15

14 $4x + 7 < 31$ (take 7)
    $4x < 31 - 7$
    $4x < 24$
     $x < 6$ (that's it)
Resist saying $x = 6$.

15 $3(2x - 5) \geq 33$ (expand the bracket)
  $6x - 15 \geq 33$ (add 15)
      $6x \geq 33 + 15$
      $6x \geq 48$
       $x \geq 8.$

1   In (a) to (d) x is an integer. List the possible values of x.

(a) $-2 < x < +3$; (b) $-1 < x \leq 4$; (c) $-2 \leq x < 0$; (d) $1 \leq x \leq 5$.

2   Solve these inequations:

(a) $5x - 3 > 22$; (b) $\frac{x}{4} + 2 < 7$; (c) $4(2x + 1) \geq 24$; (d) $7x + 2 \leq 2x - 8$.

An unusual inequation

16   Solve this inequation:
$$x^2 < 9$$ [3 marks].

In plain English, an unknown number squared is less than 9.

$x = 3$ [scores 0] (lucky to get 0)

$x < 3$ is sensible, but the fact that the question scores 3 marks should suggest that there is more to this question.

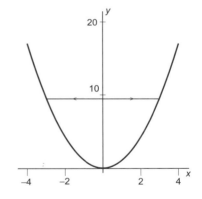

Look at this rough sketch of the curve $y = x^2$.
It shows that when $x < -3$, then $x^2 > 9$.
$(-4)^2 = 16$. This is greater than 9.

To solve our inequality *fully* you must say that x is less than 3 and also more than -3.
This is normally written $-3 < x < 3$.

17   Solve $x^2 < 5$ [3 marks].

$$\sqrt{5} = 2.24 \text{ (3 s.f.)}$$
$$\therefore -2.24 < x < 2.24$$

Note: $x = 2.24$ scores 0
          $x < 2.24$ scores only 1 out of 3.
The full range is expected.

18   $x^2 \leq 16$.

So $-4 \leq x \leq 4$ that's all.

19 $x^2 > 4$.

Now either $x > 2$ or $x < -2$.
These two parts cannot be linked together.

20 $x^2 \geq 90$.

$\sqrt{x} = 9.49$ (3 s.f.)
Either $x \geq 9.49$ or $x \leq -9.49$.

EXERCISE

E

Try these six questions. Solve the inequalities.

1 $x^2 < 100$ **2** $x^2 < 50$ **3** $x^2 \leq 49$
4 $x^2 > 25$ **5** $x^2 > 11$ **6** $x^2 \geq 144$.

Answers

Exercise A   **1** $x = 5$ **2** $x = 1$ **3** $x = 4$ **4** $x = 0$ **5** $x = 24$ **6** $x = -6$ **7** $x = 6$
          8 $x = 2$ **9** $x = 12$ **10** $x = 4.375$.

Exercise B   **1** $x = 4$ **2** $x = 3$ **3** $x = 4$ **4** $x = 10$ **5** $x = -16$ **6** $x = -1.5$ **7** $x = 7$
          8 $x = 1.5$ **9** $x = 1.25$ **10** $x = 8.75$.

Exercise C   **1** $x = 7.8$ **2** $x = 8.6$ **3** $x = 3.1$ **4** $x = 4.9$.

Exercise D   **1** (a) $x = -1, 0, 1, 2$, (b) $x = 0, 1, 2, 3, 4$, (c) $x = -2, -1$, (d) $x = 1, 2, 3, 4, 5$
          2 (a) $x > 5$, (b) $x < 20$, (c) $x \geq 2.5$, (d) $x \leq -2$.

Exercise E   **1** $-10 < x < 10$ **2** $-7.07 < x < 7.07$ **3** $-7 \leq x \leq 7$.

These answers must be linked in this way.

4 Either $x > 5$ or $x < -5$ **5** either $x > 3.32$ or $x < -3.32$ **6** either $x \geq 12$ or $x \leq -12$.

These last three answers cannot be linked.

Chapter 6

Algebraic Graphs
(with some gradient interpretation)

Essential Skills

It is important that

(a) you have met the layout of graphs involving directed numbers e.g. on this graph A is $(3, 1)$, B is $(3, -1)$, C is $(-3, 1)$ and D is $(-3, -1)$

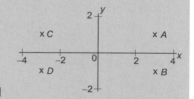

(b) you have done some basic substitution; you may need to tackle parts of Chapter 4;

(c) you know how to find the gradient of a straight line. (It will be explained anyway!)

Basic Facts

When presented graphically, equations like

(a) $y = 2x + 1$ are straight lines

(b) $y = 2x^2 + 3x - 2$ are curves called parabolas

(c) $y = \frac{30}{x}$ are curves called hyperbolas.

With many straight-line graphs the gradient has an important meaning.

Substitution

To be able to draw curves or straight-line graphs you will need to be able to substitute expertly, especially with negative numbers.

AMPLES

1–4

1   If $y = 2x + 5$ find y if (i) $x = 3$, (ii) $x = -3$.

   (i) $y = 2 \times 3 + 5$
        $y = 6 + 5 = 11$.

   (ii) $y = 2 \times -3 + 5$
        $y = -6 + 5 = -1$.

2   If $y = 3x^2$ find y when (i) $x = 2$, (ii) $x = -2$.

   (i) $y = 3 \times 2^2 = 3 \times 4 = 12$

   (ii) $y = 3 \times (-2)^2 = 3 \times 4 = 12$
        as $(-2) \times (-2) = +4$.

When many values are needed a table of values is often requested.

3   If $y = x^2 - 2x - 1$, find y if $x =$ (a) -2, (b) -1, (c) 0, (d) 1 (by completing the table below).

x	-2	-1	0	1
x^2	4	1	0	1
$-2x$	4	2	0	-2
-1	-1	-1	-1	-1
y	7	2	-1	-2

Note that the first row is simply the question repeated. The middle three rows are my working out and the final row contains the answers.

4   If $y = \frac{12}{x}$ find y when (i) $x = 2$ and (ii) $x = -3$.

(i) $y = \frac{12}{2} = 6$;   (ii) $y = \frac{12}{-3} = -4$ as $(+) \div (-) = (-)$ always.

EXERCISE

A

1   If $y = 4x - 1$ find y if (i) $x = 2$, (ii) $x = -2$.
2   If $y = x^2 - 3$ find y if (i) $x = 1$, (ii) $x = -3$.
3   If $y = x^2 - 7x + 1$, find the values of y when $x =$ (a) -2, (b) -1, (c) 0, (d) $+1$, (e) $+2$ (use a table).
4   If $y = \frac{40}{x}$ find y if (i) $x = 8$, (ii) $x = -4$.

Straight lines

Equations like (a) $y = 3x + 1$, (b) $y = -2x - 1$, (c) $4x + 3y = 24$ and (d) $2x - 5y = 10$ are all equations of straight lines. They do not contain x^2 or x^3 or dividing by x, e.g. $\frac{20}{x}$.

EXAMPLES

5–6

5   Plot the straight line graph of $y = 3x - 2$ for values of x from -2 to $+2$.

You should realise that you only need two points as it is a straight line. It is sensible to do three as you might make a small mistake. Choose simple values of x. Choose $x = 0$, 1, and 2 whenever possible. Here is my table of values.

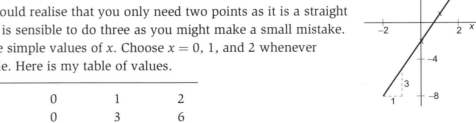

x	0	1	2
$3x$	0	3	6
-2	-2	-2	-2
y	-2	1	4

Notice that the values of y go up in threes. It is because you are doing the three times table. The little triangle at the bottom of the line shows that the gradient is also 3 (more of that later!).

6   Draw the graph of the line $2x + 3y = 12$.

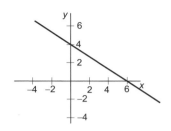

We prefer the line in the form $y = 2x + 2$ or $y = -3x - 4$, etc. When the equation is of this form, i.e. $ax + by = c$ where a, b, and c are numbers, it is better to find only two points; so do them carefully.

Start with $x = 0$ Then let $y = 0$
$\quad 0 + 3y = 12$ $\quad 2x + 0 = 12$
$\qquad y = 4$. $\qquad x = 6$.

Our table is

x	0	6
y	4	0

EXERCISE
B

Make up tables of values for each of these four straight-line graphs and draw the graphs:
1 $y = 2x$ **2** $y = -3x + 6$ **3** $4x + 5y = 20$ **4** $2y + x = 6$.

Parabolas

The most regularly requested curve is $y = x^2$.

It looks like this for values of x from -3 to 3.

You need to find far more points.
Here is the table of values.

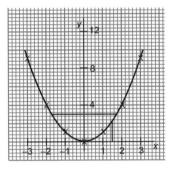

x	-3	-2	-1	0	$+1$	$+2$	$+3$
y	9	4	1	0	1	4	9

Usually you are expected to take readings from your curve,
e.g. use your curve to estimate (a) $(1.5)^2$, (b) $\sqrt{3}$.
My curve gives the answers as about (a) 2.2 and (b) 1.7 or -1.7.
The lines which have been added to the curve show you how I got these answers.

The equations of these types of curve can be more complex. Care is needed with the tables of values.

EXAMPLES
7–8

7   (a) Draw the curve $y = x^2 + 2x - 4$ for values of x from -4 to $+2$.

   (b) Use your curve to find the two solutions to the equation $x^2 + 2x - 4 = 0$.

   Here is my table. Be sure that you can see how I arrived at my figures.

---

x	-4	-3	-2	-1	0	1	2
x^2	16	9	4	1	0	1	4
$2x$	-8	-6	-4	-2	0	2	4
-4	-4	-4	-4	-4	-4	-4	-4
y	4	-1	-4	-5	-4	-1	4

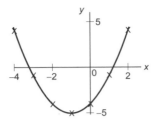

(b) When $x^2 + 2x - 4 = 0$ then $y = 0$ (on the x axis).
So $x = 1.2$ or $x = -3.2$

You may be asked to draw a curve and a straight line at the same time.

8   (a) Complete a table of values for the curve $y = 2x^2 - 3x + 1$ for x from -2 to $+4$ and sketch the curve. (b) On the same graph paper draw the straight line $y = 2x + 4$.
(c) Use your graphs to find the two solutions of the equation $2x^2 - 3x + 1 = 2x + 4$.

Here are the two tables of values:

(a)

x	-2	-1	0	1	2	3	4
$2x^2$	8	2	0	2	8	18	32
$-3x$	6	3	0	-3	-6	-9	-12
$+1$	1	1	1	1	1	1	1
y	15	6	1	0	3	10	21

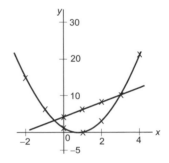

(b)

x	0	1	2
$2x$	0	2	4
$+4$	4	4	4
y	4	6	8

(c) They meet when $x = -0.5$ and $x = 3$.

EXERCISE

C

1   Sketch the curve $y = x^2 + 1$ for values of x from -3 to $+3$.
2   (a) Sketch the curve of $y = x^2 - 3x + 1$ for values of x from -2 to $+5$.
Use your curve to solve the equation $x^2 - 3x + 1 = 0$.
3   (a) On the same graph paper draw (i) the curve $y = 2x^2 + 4x - 3$ for values of x from -4 to $+2$ and (ii) the straight line $y = x + 3$. (b) Use your graph to solve the equation $2x^2 + 4x - 3 = x + 3$.

Chapter 6

The hyperbola

The graphs of equations like

$y = \frac{40}{x}$ or $y = \frac{20}{x}$ etc.

are called hyperbolas.

Their tables of values are easy to compile.
The graphs, when only positive values of x are
considered, look like this:

They are symmetrical curves.
Their axis of symmetry is the line $y = x$.

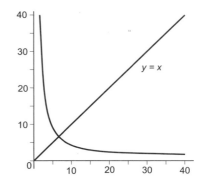

AMPLES

9–10

9 Draw the graph of the equation $y = \frac{20}{x}$ for values of x from 1 to 20.

It is normal to choose for values of x numbers which are factors of x. The table of values is:

x	1	2	4	5	10	20
y	20	10	5	4	2	1

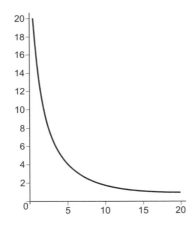

10 (a) Draw the graph of the curve $y = \frac{12}{x}$ for values of x from 1 to 12.

(b) On the same axes, draw the graph of the straight line $y = 2x + 1$.

(c) Use your graph to find a solution of the equation $\frac{12}{x} = 2x + 1$.

The tables are:

$y = \frac{12}{x}$

x	1	2	3	4	6	12
y	12	6	4	3	2	1

$y = 2x + 1$

x	0	1	2
2x	0	2	4
+ 1	+ 1	+ 1	+ 1
y	1	3	5

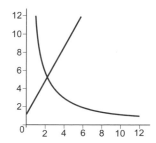

A solution is the x co-ordinate of the intersection. My graph gives $x = 2.25$.

EXERCISE

D

1   Draw the graph of $y = \frac{30}{x}$ for values of x from 1 to 30.

2   On the same axes of co-ordinates plot (a) the curve $y = \frac{48}{x}$, (b) the straight line $y = 6x + 3$. Use your graph to estimate a solution to the equation $\frac{48}{x} = 6x + 3$.

3   Plot the graph of $y = \frac{36}{x}$ for values of x from 1 to 36. On the same axes plot the straight line of equation $y = 5x$. Use your graphs to find a solution to the equation $\frac{36}{x} = 5x$.

Gradients

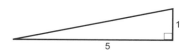

This triangle represents a hill. Its gradient is $\frac{1}{5}$ not $\frac{5}{1}$.

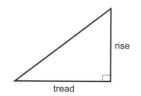

Many people remember this by thinking of a staircase.

They remember gradient $= \dfrac{\text{rise}}{\text{tread}}$.

KAMPLE

11

Look at this graph which can be used to change pounds to kilograms and vice versa. Here are four matching questions.

(a) What weight in kilograms is equivalent to 100 lb?
(b) What weight in pounds is equal to 16 kg?
(c) What weight in pounds is equal to 80 kg?
(d) What is the line's gradient and what does it represent?

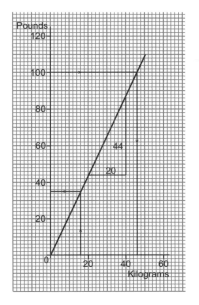

You must start by looking closely at the scale. You must realise that a small square is two units on both axes. Look at the lines which have been added to the graph. They show you how to obtain the answers, and more importantly, they earn marks from the examiner!

(a) 100 lb = 46 kg (nearest kilogram).
(b) 16 kg = 35 lb (nearest pound).
(c) 80 kg is off the scale. The reading at 40 kg is 88 lb.
     Simply double 88 as 40 is a half of 80. $2 \times 88 = 176$ lb.
(d) Gradient $= \frac{44}{20} = 2.2$. This means that 1 kg = 2.2 lb.

Distance/time graphs

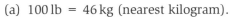

KAMPLE

12

This distance/time graph represents a motorist's $2\frac{1}{2}$ h journey on a motorway. Here are three questions:

(a) What was the time after she had travelled 90 miles?
(b) How far had she travelled by 3.42 p.m.?
(c) Calculate the gradient of this line. What does this answer represent?

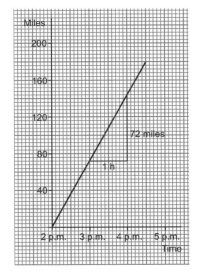

The basic scales are vital here. Every year many good students make careless errors. You must ask yourself 'what is a small square on each axis?'
In time it is 6 min, $60 \div 10$.
In distance it is 4 miles, $40 \div 10$.
Now you can start!

(a) By looking across and down I got 3.15 p.m.
(b) About 122 miles.
(c) Gradient $= \frac{72}{1}$ (see graph) = 72.

You divided distance by time. It is her speed. She was travelling at 72 m.p.h.

A ready reckoner

EXAMPLE

13

A T.V. repair man uses this graph to calculate his labour charges when he is 'called out'. Use the graph to find:

(a) the time he works if he charges £34;
(b) his charge for 40 min work;
(c) the line's gradient and its interpretation;
(d) his call out charge.

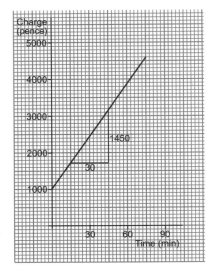

> 1 small square across is 3 min.
> 1 small square up is 100p.
> (a) 50 min. (b) 2900p or £29. (c) $\frac{1450}{30} \simeq 48$.
> This is money ÷ time. It is his rate of pay.
> He charges 48p per minute. (d) 1000p or £10.

EXAMPLE

14

An example in algebra

The equation of a straight line is $y = 3x - 1$. Draw up a table of values. Plot the graph for values of x from 0 to 3. What is the line's gradient?

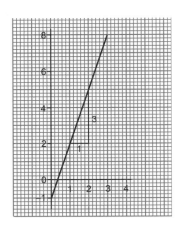

The table is:

x	0	1	2
$3x$	0	3	6
-1	-1	-1	-1
y	-1	2	5

The line is alongside.
The gradient is $\frac{3}{1} = 3$ (see graph).

1   The graph below, labelled A, converts litres to gallons and the reverse. Use the graph to:
(a) change 72 l to gallons; (b) change 144 l to gallons; (c) calculate the line's gradient and explain what it represents.

2   A motorist left Crewe at 1 p.m. and drove to Swindon at a steady speed. He arrived at 4.30 p.m. The distance between the two towns is 175 miles.
(a) Draw a straight line to illustrate his journey. Use your graph to find: (i) the time when he was 130 miles from Crewe; (ii) the distance he was from Swindon at 4.12 p.m.
(b) Calculate your line's gradient. What have you found?

3   Electricity bills have two parts: (i) the standing charge; (ii) the cost of the electricity used. The graph below, labelled B, shows the prices charged in 1997.

Use this graph to find: (i) the total bill for a customer who used 850 units; (ii) the standing charge; (iii) the line's gradient and explain its meaning.

4 Plot the straight line graph $y = 4x - 2$ for values of x from -2 to $+2$.
Use your graph to find the gradient of the line.

A   B

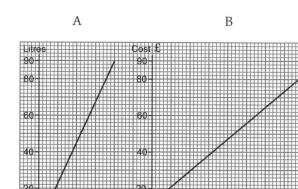

Answers

ercise A   **1** (i) 7, (ii) -9 **2** (i) -2, (ii) 6   **3** The 'y' row is 19, 9, 1, -5, -9 **4** (i) 5, (ii) -10.

ercise B   **1** Your line should go through (0, 0) (1, 2) and (2, 4)
2 This one goes through (0, 6) (1, 3) and (2, 0)
3 This time through (0, 4) and (5, 0)
4 Through (0, 3) and (6, 0).

ercise C   **2** $x = 2.6$ or $x = 0.4$ **3** $x = 1.1$ or $x = -2.6$.

ercise D   **2** $x = 2.6$ **3** $x = 2.7$.

ercise E   **1** (a) 16, (b) 32, (c) the gradient is 4.5, 4.5 l = 1 gallon   **2** (a) 3.36 p.m., (b) 15 miles (if your answer is 160 read the question again!) The gradient is 50; his speed is 50 m.p.h.
3 (i) £71.50, (ii) £12, (iii) 0.07 or $\frac{7}{100}$, each unit cost £0.07 or 7p   **4** 4.

Chapter 7

Expansions and Factors Leading to Quadratic Equations

> ### Essential Skills
>
> (a) Some knowledge of brackets.
> (b) Ease with directed numbers.
> (c) You need to know your tables.
>
> ### Basic Facts
>
> (a) Expansions will range from $3(3x + 2) = 9x + 6$ to $(x - 3)^2 = x^2 - 6x + 9$.
> (b) Factors will vary as much as from $10x - 25 = 5(2x - 5)$ to
> $12x^2y + 9xy^2 = 3xy(4x + 3y)$ and include $x^2 - 11x + 30 = (x - 5)(x - 6)$.
> (c) If a and b are numbers and $a \times b = 0$, then either $a = 0$ or $b = 0$.

Expansions

EXAMPLES

1–6

Expand the following.

1   $4(2x + 5)$. This simply means multiply the contents of the bracket by 4
   as $4 \times 2x = 8x$ and $4 \times +5 = +20$
   then $4(2x + 5) = 8x + 20$.

2   $x(x - 6)$. This is very similar;
   $x \times x = x^2$ and $x \times -6 = -6x$
   so $x(x - 6) = x^2 - 6x$.

3   $2x(3y + 5)$. This time the contents are multiplied by $2x$.
   $2x \times 3y = 6xy$ and $2x \times 5 = 10x$.
   So $2x(3y + 5) = 6xy + 10x$.

4   $(x + 7)(x + 4)$. Now all the second bracket contents must be multiplied by all the first one.
   $x \times x = x^2$ and $x \times 4 = 4x$
   $7 \times x = 7x$ and $7 \times 4 = 28$.
   Therefore $(x + 7)(x + 4) = x^2 + 4x + 7x + 28$
                             $= x^2 + 11x + 28$ as $7x + 4x = 11x$ (like terms).

5   Similarly $(x - 8)(x - 5) = x^2 - 5x - 8x + 40$
$$= x^2 - 13x + 40.$$
Note that $(-8) \times (-5) = +40$ and that $(-8) + (-5) = -13$.

6   You may be asked to expand $(x + 9)^2$.
Simply write $(x + 9)(x + 9) = x^2 + 9x + 9x + 81$
$$= x^2 + 18x + 81.$$

ERCISE

A

Expand the following:

1   $3(2x + 7)$ 2 $5(3x - 2)$ 3 $x(x + 4)$ 4 $y(y - 5)$ 5 $2x(x - 5)$
6   $3y(5 - 2y)$ 7 $(x + 6)(x + 5)$ 8 $(y + 6)(y - 2)$ 9 $(x - 8)(x + 3)$
10   $(p - 5)(p - 3)$ 11 $(x + 8)^2$ 12 $(x - 2)^2$.

Common factors

This is the complete reverse of the skills practised in the first three examples in the Expansions section. There may be 1, 2, or even 3 common factors.

MPLES

7–10

Factorise the following.

7   $12x + 30$.

You must look for common factors. There is no common letter. There are three common numbers. They are 2, 3, and 6. You **must** choose the largest.

$12x + 30 = 6(2x + 5)$.

8   $4x^2 - 10x$.

Now there are two factors. They are 2 and x. You write

$4x^2 - 10x = 2x(2x - 5)$.

9   $10a^2b - 15ab^2$.

Now 5, a and b are factors. So the answer is

$10a^2b - 15ab^2 = 5ab(2a - 3b)$. That's all.

Here is another example I prepared earlier.

10   $8x^2 + 12x$.

What are the two common factors? The highest number is 4. The letter is x.
You write $8x^2 + 12x = 4x(2x + 3)$.

Chapter 7

EXERCISE B

Factorise:

1 $4x + 6$ **2** $12y - 18$ **3** $40z + 100$ **4** $2x^2 + 10x$ **5** $6y^2 - 9y$
6 $12z^2 + 18z$ **7** $4x^2y + 2xy^2$ **8** $8a^2b - 6ab$ **9** $20x^2y^3 - 15x^3y^2$.

EXAMPLES 11–14

11 Factorise $x^2 + 8x + 12$.

Your thoughts should be:

(a) the xs are obvious;
(b) the signs are both $+$;
(c) the numbers add up to 8;
(d) the numbers multiply to 12;
(e) the numbers are 2 and 6, as $2 + 6 = 8$ and $2 \times 6 = 12$.

You only write $x^2 + 8x + 12 = (x + 2)(x + 6)$.

12 Factorise $x^2 - 10x + 21$.

(a) The signs are both $-$;
(b) the numbers multiply to 21 and add to -10;
(c) they are -3 and -7, as $(-3) + (-7) = -10$
and $(-3) \times (-7) = 21$.

You simply write $x^2 - 10x + 21 = (x - 3)(x - 7)$.

13 Factorise $x^2 + 4x - 32$.

(a) One sign is $+$, the other is $-$;
(b) the numbers multiply to -32 and add to $+4$;
(c) they are $+8$ and -4, as $(+8) + (-4) = 4$
and $(+8) \times (-4) = -32$.

So, $x^2 + 4x - 32 = (x + 8)(x - 4)$.

14 Similarly $x^2 - 3x - 54 = (x - 9)(x + 6)$.

EXERCISE C

Factorise:

1 $x^2 + 14x + 40$ **2** $x^2 + x - 12$ **3** $x^2 - 5x - 24$ **4** $x^2 - 16x + 60$.

Quadratic equations (easy factors)

15 Solve the equation $x^2 - 9x + 18 = 0$.

Firstly, factorise: $x^2 - 9x + 18 = 0$
$(x - 6)(x - 3) = 0$.

These numbers multiply to zero, therefore one of them is zero.
Either $x - 6 = 0$ or $x - 3 = 0$.
Solving separately, $x = 6$ or $x = 3$.

16 Solve $x^2 + 11x + 30 = 0$.

Factorising $(x + 6)(x + 5) = 0$, so
either $x + 6 = 0$ or $x + 5 = 0$
              $x = -6$ or $x = -5$.

17 $x^2 + 4x - 60 = 0$.

              $(x + 10)(x - 6) = 0$.
Either $x + 10 = 0$ or $x - 6 = 0$
         $x = -10$ or $x = 6$.

18 $x^2 - x - 20 = 0$.

              $(x - 5)(x + 4) = 0$.
Either $x - 5 = 0$ or $x + 4 = 0$
         $x = 5$ or $x = -4$.

19 $x^2 - 7x = 0$

              $x(x - 7) = 0$.
Either $x = 0$ or $x - 7 = 0$
         $x = 0$ or $x = 7$.

Two small points need to be noted. In example **18** the numbers add to -1, i.e. $-x(-5x + 4x)$.
In example **19**, don't overlook a common factor like x.

Solve these quadratic equations:

1 $x^2 + 11x + 18 = 0$ **2** $x^2 + 14x + 40 = 0$ **3** $x^2 - 13x + 30 = 0$
4 $x^2 - 15x + 36 = 0$ **5** $x^2 + 2x - 24 = 0$ **6** $x^2 + 3x - 28 = 0$
7 $y^2 - 3y - 70 = 0$ **8** $z^2 - 6z - 72 = 0$ **9** $x^2 - 3x = 0$ **10** $x^2 + 5x = 0$.

Answers

Exercise A

1 $6x + 21$ **2** $15x - 10$ **3** $x^2 + 4x$ **4** $y^2 - 5y$ **5** $2x^2 - 10x$ **6** $15y - 6y^2$
7 $x^2 + 11x + 30$ **8** $y^2 + 4y - 12$ **9** $x^2 - 5x - 24$ **10** $p^2 - 8p + 15$
11 $x^2 + 16x + 64$ **12** $x^2 - 4x + 4$.

Exercise B

1 $2(2x + 3)$ **2** $6(2y - 3)$ **3** $20(2z + 5)$ **4** $2x(x + 5)$ **5** $3y(2y - 3)$
6 $6z(2z + 3)$ **7** $2xy(2x + y)$ **8** $2ab(4a - 3)$ **9** $5x^2y^2(4y - 3x)$.

Exercise C

1 $(x + 10)(x + 4)$ **2** $(x + 4)(x - 3)$ **3** $(x - 8)(x + 3)$ **4** $(x - 6)(x - 10)$.

Exercise D

1 $x = -2$ or -9 **2** $x = -4$ or -10 **3** $x = 3$ or 10 **4** $x = 3$ or 12
5 $x = -6$ or 4 **6** $x = -7$ or 4 **7** $y = 10$ or -7 **8** $z = 12$ or -6 **9** $x = 0$ or 3
10 $x = 0$ or -5.

Chapter 8

Indices

Essential Skills

It would help if you have met words like squared and cubed and have seen expressions like x^2 or 10^3.

Basic Facts

1. Two laws of indices will be tested. Written formally they are:
   (1) $x^a \times x^b = x^{a+b}$
   (2) $x^a \div x^b = x^{a-b}$.
   These two examples show what this means.
   (a) Simplify $2^4 \times 2^2 = (2 \times 2 \times 2 \times 2) \times (2 \times 2) = 2^6$.
       The powers have been added.
   (b) Simplify $3^5 \div 3^3 = \frac{3^5}{3^3} = \frac{3 \times 3 \times 3 \times 3 \times 3}{3 \times 3 \times 3} = 3^2$.
       This time the indices have been subtracted.

2. A negative index gives a fraction, e.g. $3^{-2} = \frac{1}{3^2} = \frac{1}{9}$.

3. A special case. As $3^2 \div 3^2 = 3^0$ and clearly $9 \div 9 = 1$ then $3^0 = 1$.
   It follows that $2^0 = 1$ and $4^0 = 1$, etc.

Simplifying expressions

The examples may be straightforward.
Simplify $x^6 \times x^4$.
It equals $x^{6+4} = x^{10}$.
Simplify $y^9 \div y^3 = y^{9-3} = y^6$.

Both these skills may be combined.

Simplify $\dfrac{x^4 \times x^3}{x^2}$

$$= \frac{x^{4+3}}{x^2} = \frac{x^7}{x^2} = x^{7-2} = x^5.$$

Sometimes numbers are considered at the same time. Treat the numbers as numbers and the indices as indices.

Chapter 8

Simplify $12x^8 \div 3x^6$.

$12x^8 \div 3x^6 = 4x^2$ because $12 \div 3 = 4$ (numbers) and $x^8 \div x^6 = x^{8-6}$ (indices).

Simplify $5x^4 \times 3x^3$.
$5x^4 \times 3x^3 = 15x^7$ as $5 \times 3 = 15$ and $x^4 \times x^3 = x^7$.

This question is about as hard as this topic can become: simplify
$\frac{5x^3 \times 4x^7}{10x^6}$. $\frac{5x^3 \times 4x^7}{10x^6} = 2x^4$ as $5 \times 4 \div 10 = 2$ and $x^{3+7-6} = x^4$.

EXERCISE

A

Simplify:

1 $x^6 \times x^3$ **2** $y^7 \times y^3$ **3** $x^8 \div x^2$ **4** $y^9 \div y^4$ **5** $\frac{x^6 \times x^4}{x^2}$ **6** $\frac{x^7 \times x^2}{x^3}$
7 $20x^6 \div 5x^2$ **8** $5x^5 \times 4x^4$ **9** $\frac{9x^4 \times 4x^2}{6x^5}$ **10** $\frac{10x^5 \times 4x}{8x^4}$.

Examples with numbers

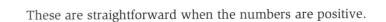

These are straightforward when the numbers are positive.

EXAMPLE

1

Find the values of (a) 10^3 (b) 2^5 (c) 5^2 (d) 8^0.

(a) $10 \times 10 \times 10 = 1000$
(b) $2 \times 2 \times 2 \times 2 \times 2 = 32$
(c) $5 \times 5 = 25$
(d) $8^0 = 1$ (see basic facts).

When the index is negative you have to realise that you are working with fractions.

EXAMPLE

2

Find the values of (a) 4^{-2} (b) 2^{-3} (c) 5^{-1}.

(a) $4^{-2} = \frac{1}{4^2} = \frac{1}{16}$
(b) $2^{-3} = \frac{1}{2^3} = \frac{1}{8}$
(c) $5^{-1} = \frac{1}{5^1} = \frac{1}{5}$.

EXERCISE

B

Find the values of:

1 10^2 **2** 4^3 **3** 2^4 **4** 5^3 **5** 10^0 **6** 5^{-2} **7** 3^{-1} **8** 5^{-3}.

Answers

Exercise A **1** x^9 **2** y^{10} **3** x^6 **4** y^5 **5** x^8 **6** x^6 **7** $4x^4$ **8** $20x^9$ **9** $6x$ **10** $5x^2$.

Exercise B **1** 100 **2** 64 **3** 16 **4** 125 **5** 1 **6** $\frac{1}{25}$ **7** $\frac{1}{3}$ **8** $\frac{1}{125}$.

Chapter 9

Simultaneous Equations

Essential Skills

(a) Ease with directed numbers.

(b) No fear of substitution.

(c) Understanding that:

if $\qquad x + y = 20$

then $\quad 2x + 2y = 40 \qquad$ (everything multiplied by 2)

or $\qquad 3x + 3y = 60 \qquad (\times 3)$

and so on.

(d) You will need to know how to plot straight-line graphs.

Basic Facts

$$4x + 3y = 25 \qquad \textbf{(1)}$$
$$x + y = 7 \qquad \textbf{(2)}$$

are said to be a pair of simultaneous equations. **(1)** and **(2)** are labels which make working clearer.

Such pairs can be:
(a) added together;
(b) subtracted from each other;
(c) 'altered' using skill (c) above.

The main skill is to **eliminate** x or y from your pair of equations, reducing them to a simple linear equation.

These types of equation can be solved graphically.

EXAMPLES

1–3

1 $\quad 4x + 2y = 20 \qquad \textbf{(1)}$

$\quad 2x + 2y = 12 \qquad \textbf{(2)}$

Think like this: there is a $+2y$ in each.
Take them away.

$\qquad 2x = 8$

$\qquad x = 4.$

Substitute in **(1)**:

$\quad 16 + 2y = 20$

$\qquad 2y = 20 - 16$

$\qquad 2y = 4$

$\qquad y = 2.$

Both known, so that's it.

2 $\quad 5x + 3y = 28 \qquad \textbf{(1)}$

$\quad x - 3y = 2 \qquad \textbf{(2)}$

This time, $+3y$ and $-3y$ add to 0.
Therefore, add these equations.

Add **(1)** and **(2)** to eliminate y:

$\qquad 6x = 30$

$\qquad x = 5.$

Substitute in (1):
$$25 + 3y = 28$$
$$3y = 28 - 25$$
$$3y = 3$$
$$y = 1.$$

3    $5x - 3y = 27$ (1) $-3y$ and $-3y$ are the same.
     $2x - 3y = 9$ (2)   So **subtract**.

Take (2) from (1):
$$3x = 18$$
$$x = 6.$$

Substitute in (1):
$$30 - 3y = 27$$
$$-3y = 27 - 30$$
$$-3y = -3$$
$$y = +1$$ as $(-) \times (+) = (-)$.

So you can either add or subtract the equations.

EXERCISE A

Try these three questions:

1    $5x + 3y = 18$ 2 $7x - 2y = 45$ 3 $5x + 4y = 41$
     $x + 3y = 6$ $x - 2y = 3$ $3x - 4y = -1.$

EXAMPLES 4–5

Unfortunately:

4    $5x + 2y = 60$ (1)
     $x + y = 15$ (2)

It is no use adding or subtracting. Neither x nor y will be eliminated. We need $5x$ or $2y$ in (2) as well.
Fortunately as $x + y = 15$
                     $2x + 2y = 30$ (all doubled).
The solution is set out like this:
              $5x + 2y = 60$ (1)
              $x + y = 15$ (2)
Multiply (2) by 2:
              $5x + 2y = 60$ (1)
              $2x + 2y = 30$ (3)   It's the same as examples **1** and **2** now.
Subtract: $3x = 30$
                 $x = 10.$
Substitute in (1):
              $50 + 2y = 60$
              $2y = 60 - 50$
              $2y = 10$
              $y = 5.$

5 $11x + 3y = 53$ **(1)**
   $3x - y = 9$ **(2)**

If we multiply **(2)** by 3,   then **(1)** will have $3y$
                and **(2)** will have $-3y$.

Solution: $11x + 3y = 53$ **(1)**
                  $3x - y = 9$ **(2)**

$\times$ **(2)** by 3: $11x + 3y = 53$ **(1)**
                  $9x - 3y = 27$ **(3)**

Add: $20x = 80$
             $x = 4.$

Substitute in **(1)**:

$$44 + 3y = 53$$
$$3y = 53 - 44$$
$$3y = 9$$
$$y = 3.$$

EXERCISE B

Try these three:

1 $4x + 3y = 25$ 2 $5x + 4y = 29$ 3 $5x - 4y = 17$
   $x + y = 7.$ $x - 2y = 3.$ $x - y = 3.$

EXAMPLES 6–7

At worst two new equations are needed:

6 $4x + 3y = 43$ **(1)**
  $3x - 2y = 28$ **(2)**

There is no way that y can be eliminated by multiplying **(2)** by a whole number. However, as 3 and 2 go into 6, we can find **two** new equations.

Solution: $4x + 3y = 43$ **(1)**
              $3x - 2y = 28$ **(2)**

Multiply **(1)** by 2 and **(2)** by 3:
              $8x + 6y = 86$ **(3)**
              $9x - 6y = 84$ **(4)**

Add **(3)** and **(4)**: $17x = 170$
              $x = 10.$

Substitute in **(1)**:

$$40 + 3y = 43$$
$$3y = 43 - 40$$
$$3y = 3$$
$$y = 1.$$

Chapter 9

7   $2x + 11y = 112$ **(1)**   Two new equations are vital. $10x$ or
      $5x + 4y = 45$ **(2)** $44y$ are possible. Choose the smaller.

Multiply **(1)** by 5 and **(2)** by 2:
$$10x + 55y = 560 \quad \textbf{(3)}$$
$$10x + 8y = 90 \quad \textbf{(4)}$$

Take **(4)** from **(3)**:
$$47y = 470$$
$$y = 10.$$

Substitute in **(1)**:
$$2x + 110 = 112$$
$$2x = 112 - 110$$
$$2x = 2$$
$$x = 1.$$

EXERCISE C

Try these two questions:

1   $5x + 3y = 59$ 2 $3x + 8y = 14$
    $3x - 2y = 24$ $5x + 3y = 13.$

EXERCISE D

This final exercise covers all the skills in this section.

1   $7x + 2y = 65$ 2 $5x + 3y = 49$
    $x - 2y = 7$ $x + y = 11$

3   $4x + 5y = 50$ 4 $3x + 11y = 53$
    $7x - 2y = 66$ $2x + 9y = 42.$

An alternative method

Sometimes you will be asked to solve equations by drawing two straight-line graphs. You may need to read some of the work in Chapter 6. Only use this method if the examiner insists. It is not for you to choose the method.

EXAMPLES

8–9

8 Solve the following pair of simultaneous equations by drawing two straight-line graphs:

$$4x + 3y = 24$$
$$x + y = 7.$$

As these are straight lines only two points are needed.
In this case let $x = 0$ then let $y = 0$.
The tables of values are:

(a)

x	0	6
y	8	0

(b)

x	0	7
y	7	0

The point where they meet is the solution. It is marked A on the graph. The answer is $x = 3$ and $y = 4$.

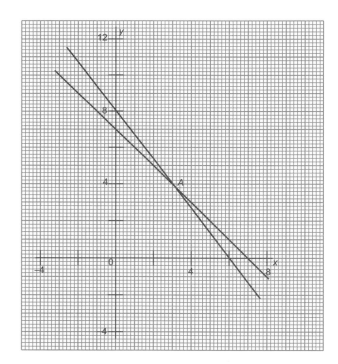

9   Solve the following pair of simultaneous equations graphically:

$y = 3x + 2$
$y = x - 1.$

As in this case y is the subject it is easier to choose values of x; usually $x = 0$, 1, and 2. Here are the two tables:

(a)

x	0	1	2
y	2	5	8

(b)

x	0	1	2
y	−1	0	1

In the examination you will draw a much larger graph than the one that is in this book. Try to read your answer to a half of a small square. These lines meet when $x = -1.5$ and $y = -2.5$.

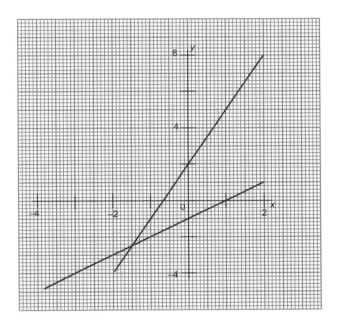

Solve both these pairs of simultaneous equations graphically.

EXERCISE
E

1   $3x + 2y = 6$
    $2x + y = 5$

2   $y = 2x + 1$
    $y = 4x - 2.$

Answers

Exercise **A**   **1** $x = 3, y = 1$ **2** $x = 7, y = 2$ **3** $x = 5, y = 4$.

Exercise **B**   **1** $x = 4, y = 3$ **2** $x = 5, y = 1$ **3** $x = 5, y = 2$.

Exercise **C**   **1** $x = 10, y = 3$ **2** $x = 2, y = 1$.

Exercise **D**   **1** $x = 9, y = 1$ **2** $x = 8, y = 3$ **3** $x = 10, y = 2$ **4** $x = 3, y = 4$.

Exercise **E**   **1** $x = 4, y = -3$ **2** $x = 1.5, y = 4$.

Chapter 10

Lines and Angles

Angles at a point

A quick recap:

Use your protractor to measure angles a and b above.

Is it clear in your mind which one is the acute angle? The parallel lines confuse some students, who assume that angle a = angle b. It is important that your realise, before you reach for your protractor, that:

angle a is acute   (between 0° and 90°), and
angle b is obtuse   (between 90° and 180°).

In fact, angle $a = 60°$ and angle $b = 120°$.

Angles at a point add up to 360°.

$$a° + b° + c° + d° = 360°$$

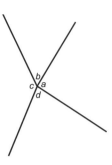

EXAMPLES

1–4

These four examples are **not** to scale. Find x, y, etc. in each diagram.

1

$$\begin{aligned} x + 40 &= 360 \\ x &= 360 - 40 \\ &= 320°. \end{aligned}$$

2

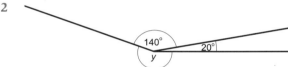

$$\begin{aligned} y + 20 + 140 &= 360 \\ y &= 360 - 160 \\ &= 200°. \end{aligned}$$

3

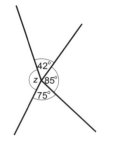

$$\begin{aligned} z + 42 + 85 + 75 &= 360 \\ z + 202 &= 360 \\ z &= 360 - 202 \\ &= 158°. \end{aligned}$$

4

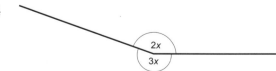

$$\begin{aligned} 3x + 2x &= 360 \\ 5x &= 360 \\ x &= \tfrac{360}{5} \\ x &= 72°. \end{aligned}$$ From this $2x = 144°$ and $3x = 216°$.

Using a protractor

These two diagrams are to scale. In each case, measure x and calculate y.

5

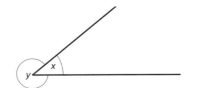

Your thoughts should be: 'x is acute, say 30°'.
Using your protractor: $x = 40°$
From this, y is given by: $y = 360 - 40$
                                                     $= 320°$.

6

Your thoughts: 'This time y is obtuse, say 160°'.
Using your protractor: $x = 120°$
Calculating y: $y = 360 - 120$
                                      $= 240°$.

Try these four similar questions. Only question 1 is to scale.

1 Measure x, calculate y.

In questions 2, 3 and 4, calculate the values of the angles marked x, y, etc.

2

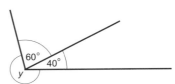

3

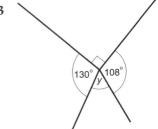

4

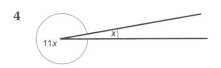

11x

Angles on a straight line

AB is a straight line. Angles on a straight line add up to 180°.

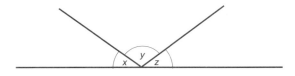

$x + y + z = 180°$

Here are some examples (**not** to scale). No protractors. In each case PQ is a straight line.

7

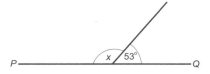

$$x = 180 - 53$$
$$= 127°.$$

8

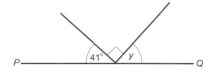

$$y + 41 + 90 = 180$$
$$y = 180 - 131$$
$$= 49°.$$

In these two examples PQ and RS are both straight lines.

9 Find the values of x and y.

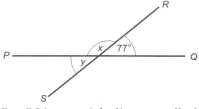

$$x = 180 - 77$$
$$= 103° \qquad \text{(straight line).}$$

But RS is a straight line as well, therefore:

$$y = 180 - 103$$
$$= 77°.$$

It is obvious (by inspection) that y is 77°. The angles y and 77° in the diagram are said to be 'vertically opposite'. Such angles are always equal.

Chapter 10

10 Find the values of x, $3x$ and y.

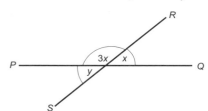

$$3x + x = 180$$
$$4x = 180$$
$$x = \frac{180}{4} = 45°$$
$$3x = 135°$$
$$y = 45° \text{ as well}$$
(vertically opposite).

ERCISE

B

Find the angles marked x, y, etc.

1

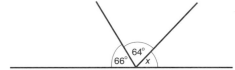

2

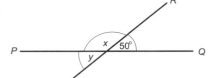

3

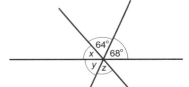

4

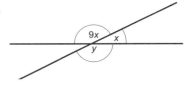

Parallel lines

In this diagram PQ and RS are parallel lines. Consider the four acute angles a, b, c and d. We already known that $a = b$ and $c = d$ (both are pairs of vertically opposite angles).

As the lines are parallel, $a = c$.

The angles are said to be *corresponding*, so

$a = b = c = d$

The four obtuse angles in the diagram must also equal each other.

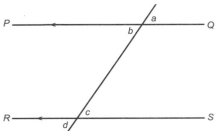

Here is a piece of the diagram drawn again:

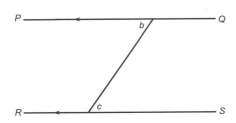

Now (a) there are no corresponding angles, and
       (b) there are no vertically opposite angles.

But $b = c$ just the same. They are called *alternate* angles.

An aid to memory

Vertically opposite angles are equal. They are called 'X' angles.

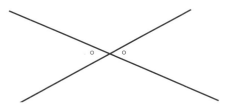

Here are four views of corresponding angles. They are called 'F' angles.

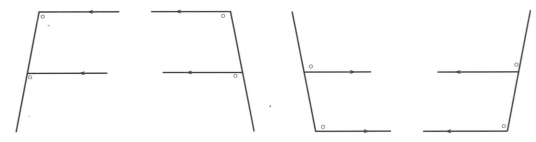

Here are too examples of alternate angles. They are called 'Z' angles.

X angles are always equal
F angles are always equal
Z angles are always equal

Note: don't provide reasons in the examination, unless they are requested.

11 Find x, y, a and b.

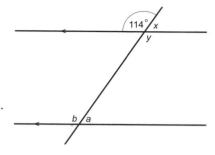

$$x = 66° \quad \text{(straight line)}$$
$$y = 114° \quad \text{(X angle)}$$
$$a = 66° \quad \text{(F angle)}$$
$$b = 114° \quad \text{(F angle or straight line)}.$$

12 Find the values of x, $4x$, y and z.

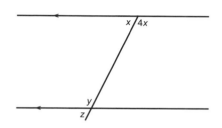

$$4x + x = 180 \quad \text{(straight line)}$$
$$5x = 180$$
$$x = 36°$$
$$4x = 144°$$
$$y = 144° \quad \text{(Z angle)}$$
$$z = 36°.$$

1 Give mathematical reasons why:

(a) $a = b$

(b) $b = c$

(c) $a = c$.

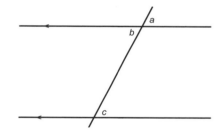

2 (a) Find a, b, c and d.

(b) What should your four answers add up to?

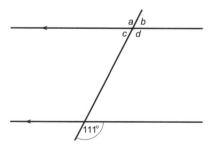

3 Find x, $5x$, $7x$, p and q.

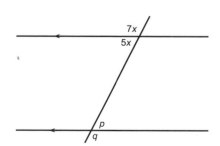

Three-figure bearings

Bearings (directions) are usually given by simply using three figures. The angles are measured *clockwise of North*. In each of these five examples the bearings are given *from* the point A *to* the point B.

13 A bearing of 180°.

This bearing is usually called South, of course.

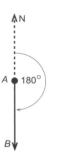

14 A bearing of 070°.

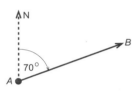

The first zero **must not** be omitted. To call this a bearing of 70° is wrong.

15 A bearing of 230°.

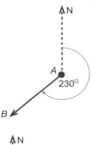

16 A bearing of 121°.

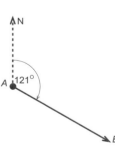

17 A bearing of 342°.

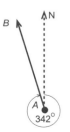

Note that example **15** was drawn by realising that 230° was 50° further clockwise than South, and **17** was drawn 18° anticlockwise of North. However, the bearings are *always* given clockwise of North.

1 The five bearings of *Y* from *X* are:

A	137°	**B**	250°
C	195°	**D**	017°	**E** 343°

and have been sketched below. They are out of order. Which is which?

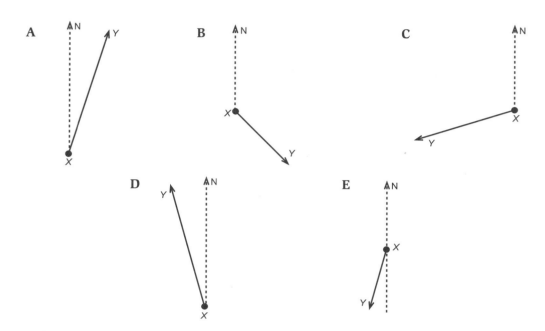

2 Use your protractor to help you find these four bearings of *P* from *Q*.

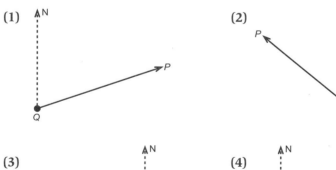

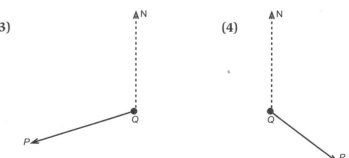

3 *A*, *B*, *C* and *D* represent four points on a map. Use your protractor to estimate these three-figure bearings:

    (a)   *A* from *D*   (b)   *B* from *A*   (c)   *C* from *B*

    (d)   *D* from *C*   (e)   *D* from *A*.

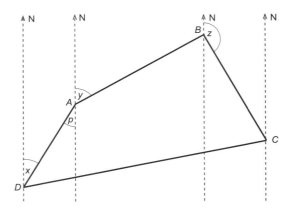

Note: in the examination you will have to draw in these (dotted) 'North lines' for yourself.

EXERCISE

E

This miscellaneous exercise covers all the topics in this chapter.

1 Use your protractor to measure angle
   a and calculate angle *b*.

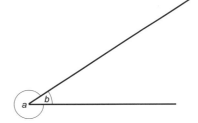

The next five questions are **not** to scale. Do not use a protractor. Calculate the angles marked *x*,
y, etc. in each of them.

2

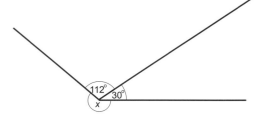

3

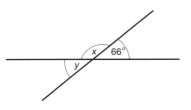

4

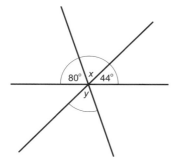

5

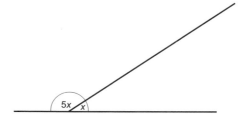

6

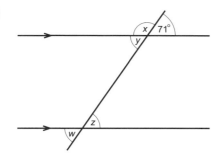

7 Give mathematical reasons why: (a) in question 4, $x = y$; (b) in question 6, $w = y$; (c) in question 6, $y = z$.

8 Arthur walks to three different places daily. This rough map illustrates these three walks:

C represents his church;
H represents his local, The Horseshoe;
B represents his bowling club;
A represents his home.

Use your protractor to calculate the bearings from Arthur's home of:

(a) the church
(b) The Horseshoe
(c) the bowling club.

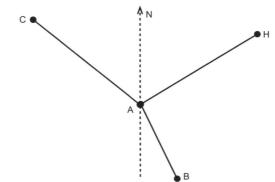

Answers

Exercise **A**   **1** $x = 78°$, $y = 282°$ **2** $y = 260°$ **3** $y = 32°$ **4** $x = 30°$, $11x = 330°$.

Exercise **B**   **1** $x = 50°$ **2** $x = 130°$, $y = 50°$ **3** $x = 48°$, $y = 68°$, $z = 64°$
4 $x = 18°$, $9x = 162°$, $y = 162°$.

Exercise **C**   **1** (a) Vertically opposite; (b) alternate; (c) corresponding. Please note that X, Z, and F angles are
not acceptable as reasons. They just help you to spot equal angles.
2 (a) $a = 111°$, $b = 69°$, $c = 69°$, $d = 111°$, (b) 360°
3 $x = 15°$, $5x = 75°$, $7x = 105°$, $p = 75°$, $q = 105°$.

Exercise **D**   **1** 137° is **B**, 250° is **C**, 195° is **E**, 017° is **A** and 343° is **D**
2 (1) 070°, (2) 310°, (3) 250°, (4) 128°; (a) 031°, (b) 061°, (c) 150°, (d) 259°, (e) 211°.

Exercise **E**   **1** $a = 34°$, $b = 326°$ **2** $x = 218°$ **3** $x = 114°$, $y = 66°$ **4** $x = 56°$, $y = 56°$
5 $x = 30°$, $5x = 150°$ **6** $x = 109°$, $y = w = z = 71°$ **7** (a) vertically opposite,
(b) corresponding, (c) alternate   **8** (a) 309°, (b) 060°, (c) 156°.

Chapter 11

The Angles of the Triangle

Three angles of a triangle

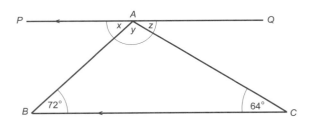

ABC is a triangle. Angle $B = 72°$, Angle $C = 64°$.
If *PQ* is parallel to *BC*, find x, y and z.

$$
\begin{aligned}
x &= 72° &&\text{(alternate or Z angles)} \\
z &= 64° &&\text{(as above)} \\
x + y + z &= 180 &&\text{(straight line)} \\
\therefore y &= 180 - 72 - 64 \\
&= 44°.
\end{aligned}
$$

But, more importantly, the three angles of the triangle add up to 180°. This illustrates and 'nearly proves' that the angles of a triangle add up to 180°.

Scalene triangles

EXAMPLES

1–4

These are triangles with all sides of different lengths.

1 Calculate the value of x.

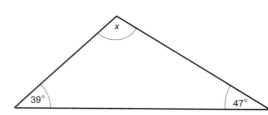

$$x + 39 + 47 = 180 \quad \text{(3 angles add to } 180°)$$
$$x + 86 = 180$$
$$x = 94°.$$

2 Find the three angles of this triangle.

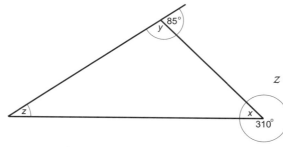

$$x = 360 - 310 \quad \text{(angles at a point)}$$
$$= 50°$$
$$y = 180 - 85 \quad \text{(straight line)}$$
$$= 95°$$
$$z + 50 + 95 = 180 \quad \text{(3 angles of a } \triangle)$$
$$z = 180 - 145$$
$$= 35°.$$

3 Find the three angles of this triangle.

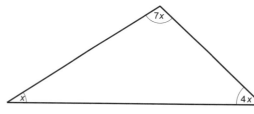

$$x + 4x + 7x = 180 \quad \text{(3 angles of a } \triangle)$$
$$12x = 180$$
$$x = 15°$$
$$4x = 60°$$
$$7x = 105°.$$

4 Find the two unknown angles.

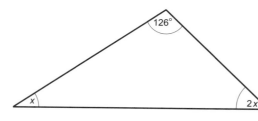

$$x + 2x + 126 = 180 \quad \text{(3 angles of a } \triangle)$$
$$3x = 180 - 126$$
$$3x = 54$$
$$x = 18°$$
$$2x = 36°.$$

Isosceles and equilateral triangles

ABC is an isosceles triangle. In this case $AB = AC$.
It is a symmetrical shape.

Clearly, angle B = angle C.

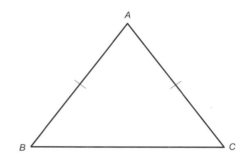

MPLES

5–8

5 Find angles Q and R.

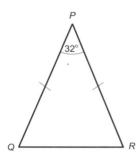

$PQ = PR$, angle $P = 32°$.
As $PQ = PR$, angle Q = angle R.

Let them both be x:

$$x + x + 32 = 180$$
$$2x = 180 - 32$$
$$2x = 148$$
$$x = 74°.$$

6 Find angle A.

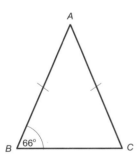

$AB = AC$, angle $B = 66°$.
As $AB = AC$, angle B = angle C
∴ angle $C = 66°$ as well.
So:

$$\text{angle } A + 66 + 66 = 180$$
$$\text{angle } A = 180 - 132$$
$$= 48°.$$

7

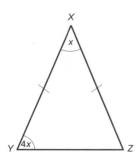

$XY = XZ$, angle $Y = 4x$, angle $X = x$
angle Y = angle $Z = 4X$.
So:

$$4x + 4x + x = 180$$
$$9x = 180$$
$$x = 20°$$
$$4x = 80°.$$

8 This is an equilateral triangle. $AB = AC = BC$.

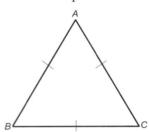

The three angles are equal.
$180 \div 3 = 60$.
They are all 60°.

EXERCISE

A

Calculate the angles x, y, z, etc.

1

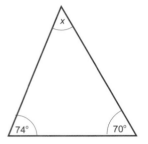

2

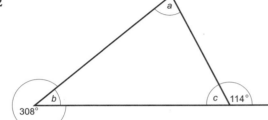

3

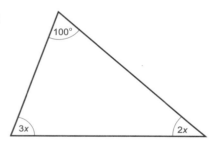

4

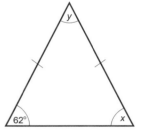

5

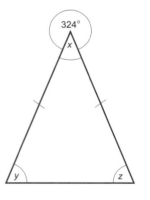

6

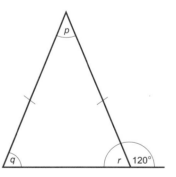

7

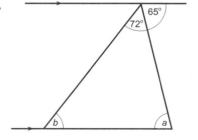

8

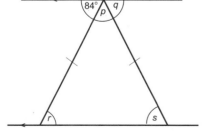

Answers

ercise **A**

1 $x = 36°$ **2** $a = 62°$, $b = 52°$, $c = 66°$ **3** $x = 16°$, $2x = 32°$, $3x = 48°$

4 $x = 62°$, $y = 56°$ **5** $x = 36°$, $y = z = 72°$ **6** all $60°$

7 $a = 65°$, $b = 43°$ **8** $r = s = q = 84°$, $p = 12°$.

Chapter 12

Angles of Quadrilaterals and Polygons

Any quadrilateral

ABCD is a quadrilateral: the angles of the triangle *ABC* add up to 180°;
the angles of the triangle *ADC* add up to 180°.

Therefore, the four angles of *ABCD* add up to 360°.

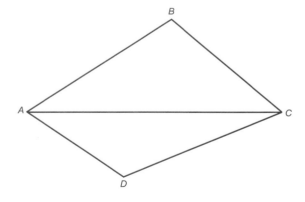

EXAMPLES

1–2   In all the following examples, the reasons are provided to help you. Only give reasons in the
examination when they are requested.

1 Find the value of x in this quadrilateral.

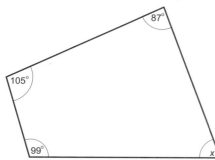

$$99 + 105 + 87 = 291$$
$$x = 360 - 291 \text{ (all 4 add up to } 360°)$$
$$x = 69°.$$

2 Two angles of this quadrilateral are 126° and 94°. The other two are equal. Find x.

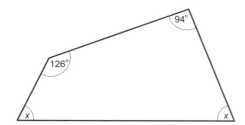

$$94 + 126 = 220$$
$$2x = 360 - 220$$
$$x = 70°.$$

The square

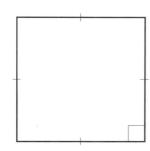

All its sides are equal.
All its angles are right angles.

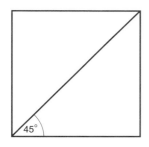

A diagonal cuts the square into two identical isosceles triangles. The right angles are bisected. There are four angles of 45° in the sketch.

As the triangles are identical, they are said to be *congruent*.

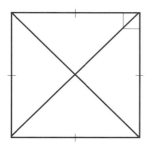

When both diagonals are drawn, eight angles of 45° can be seen and there are four small congruent isosceles triangles.

The rectangle

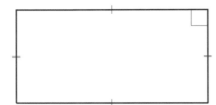

Opposite sides are equal.

All angles are 90°.

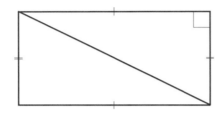

The diagonal cuts the rectangle into two congruent scalene triangles.

There are no angles of 45° here. The angles depend on the shape of the rectangle.

The parallelogram

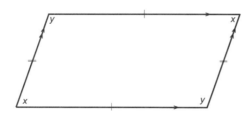

The opposite sides are parallel.
The opposite sides are equal in length.
The opposite angles are equal.

As $2x + 2y = 360°$ (four angles of a quadrilateral)
$x + y = 180°$ (half of everything).

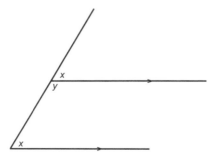

This is a drawing of the left-hand side of our parallelogram.

The two x angles are corresponding. This confirms that $x + y = 180°$.

3 Find the four angles of this parallelogram.

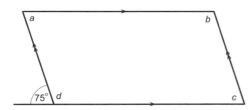

An exterior angle of 75° is given (see diagram)

$$d = 180 - 75 \quad \text{(straight line)}$$
$$= 105°$$
$$b = 105° \qquad \text{(opposite angle)}.$$
$$\text{But } a + d = 180° \qquad \text{(shown earlier)}.$$
$$\text{Therefore } a = 75° \qquad \text{(alternate angles as well)}$$
$$\text{and } c = 75°.$$

4 The obtuse angle of a parallelogram is three times its acute angle (see diagram). Find the four angles of this parallelogram.

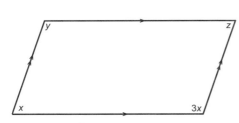

$$x + 3x = 180 \qquad \text{(as shown)}$$
$$\therefore 4x = 180$$
$$x = 45°$$
$$3x = 135°$$
$$y = 135° \qquad \text{(opposite)}$$
$$z = 45°.$$

The rhombus

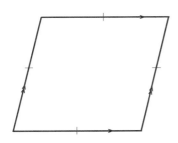

The rhombus is a parallelogram which has all its sides equal.

It is symmetrical about its diagonals.

These diagonals bisect one another at right angles, and they bisect the four angles of the rhombus. Again we have four congruent triangles.

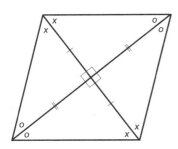

EXAMPLES

5–7

5 Find the four angles of this rhombus.

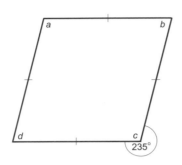

In this case we use the properties of the parallelogram.

$$c = 360 - 235 \quad \text{(angles at a point)}$$
$$= 125°$$
$$a = 125° \quad \text{(opposite)}$$
$$b = d = 55°.$$

6 *ABCD* is a rhombus. Angle $A = 108°$. Find the three angles of the triangle *BCD*.

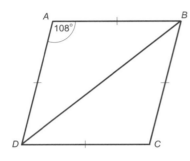

Start with a sketch.
   Angle $BCD = 108°$ (opposite).
   Angle DBC = Angle BDC (isosceles triangle).
Therefore,
   angle $DBC = 72 \div 2 = 36°$
   angle $BDC = 36°$.

7 *PQRS* (see diagram) is a rhombus. Its diagonals cross at *T*. If the exterior angle at *S* is 110°, find the three angles of triangle *PTQ*.

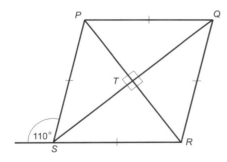

Angle $PSR = 70°$.
Diagonal *SQ* bisects this angle; therefore
   angle PST = angle $RST = 35°$
   angle PQT = angle $RQT = 35°$ as well.
Therefore, the angles are:
   angle $PQT = 35°$
   angle $PTQ = 90°$ (a property)
   angle $QPT = 55°$ (3rd angle of the △).

The trapezium

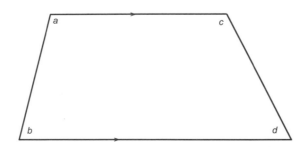

One pair of sides is parallel; that's all.

However, it can be shown by corresponding angles that:

$$a + b = 180°$$
$$c + d = 180°.$$

There is no link between a and c, etc.

AMPLE

8

Find the four angles of this trapezium.

Clearly $y = 180 - 63$
$$= 117°$$

$$x = 63° \qquad \text{(alternate)}.$$

Considering the right-hand side independently:

$$4a + a = 180$$
$$5a = 180$$
$$a = 36°$$

$$4a = 144°.$$

Two exercises follow. Exercise A covers the geometry of this topic. Exercise B applies this work to trigonometry and Pythagoras' theorem and is relatively difficult.

ERCISE

A

Reason out the angles marked a, b, c, etc. in these diagrams.

1
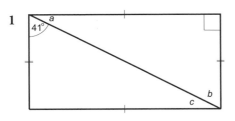

2
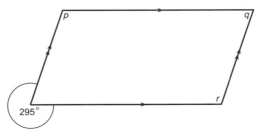

3
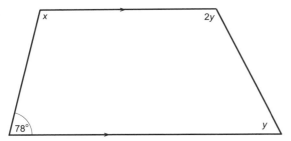

4
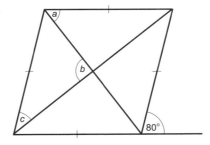

5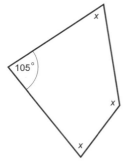

6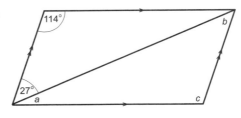

7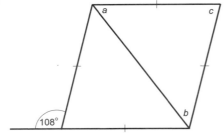

8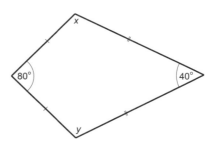

9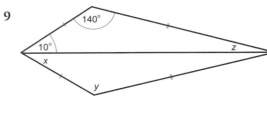

10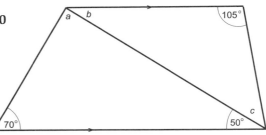

11 In questions 1, 6, 7, 9 and 10 the quadrilateral has been cut into two triangles by drawing a diagonal. In which of these questions are the triangles congruent?

EXERCISE

B

1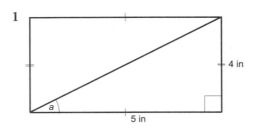

Find:
(a) the length of the diagonal of this rectangle;
(b) the size of the angle marked a.

2

10 cm   10 cm

16 cm

10 cm   10 cm

The diagram represents a rhombus with sides of 10 cm whose longer diagonal is 16 cm long. Find the length of the shorter diagonal.

3

A _____ B

9 cm

80°
D _____ C
12 cm

ABCD is a parallelogram where AD = 9 cm, DC = 12 cm and angle ADC = 80°.

Calculate (i) the height of the parallelogram;
(ii) its area.

Polygons

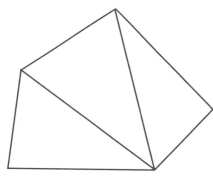

This is an irregular polygon. It has five sides.
As you can see it is the same as three triangles (5−2).
Its angles must add to 180° × 3 = 540° as the angles of one triangle add to 180°.

Similarly, a six-sided shape would cut into four triangles (6−2). Its angles add to 180° × 4 = 720°.
It follows that a seven-sided shape is five triangles. Its total is 5 × 180° = 900°.

An octagon (eight sides) must be six triangles. 180° × 6 = 1080° and so on!
The fact that the total of the exterior angles is always 360° can also help you.

MPLES

9–11

9   Four interior angles of a pentagon are 80°, 90°, 105° and 120°. Find the fifth angle.

The four angles we know add to 395°. All five add to 540°. So the fifth is 540°−395° = 145°.

10 Find the size of an interior angle of a regular hexagon (six sides).

If a shape is described as regular then all its sides are equal and all its angles are equal. We know that the angles add to 720° so each is 720° ÷ 6 = 120°. That's all!

11 A ten-sided polygon is regular. (a) Find the size of one of its exterior angles. (b) Use the answer to (a) to find the size of an interior angle. (c) Find the interior angle again using a second and completely different method.

This is a sketch of a piece of this polygon. It shows that $x + y = 180°$. They form a straight line. Clearly an interior angle and an exterior angle add to 180° always.

There are ten exterior angles and they are equal to each other.

(a) Each exterior angle must be $360° \div 10 = 36°$.
(b) Each interior angle must be $180° - 36° = 144°$.
(c) This ten-sided shape would cut into eight triangles. $180° \times 8 = 1440°$.

Each interior angle would be $1440 \div 10 = 144°$ (as before).

EXERCISE
C

1 Five angles of a hexagon are 100°, 110°, 120°, 130°, and 135°. Find the size of the sixth angle.
2 Find the size of an interior angle of a regular octagon (eight sides).
3 (a) Find the size of an exterior angle of a regular nine-sided figure. (b) Use your answer to find the size of an interior angle.
4 One angle of a pentagon is 100°. The other four are equal. What is the size of each of them?

Answers

Exercise A
1 $a = 49°$, $b = 41°$, $c = 49°$ 2 $p = 115°$, $q = 65°$, $r = 115°$
3 $x = 102°$, $y = 60°$, $2y = 120°$ 4 $a = 50°$, $b = 90°$, $c = 40°$
5 $x = 85°$ 6 $a = 39°$, $b = 27°$, $c = 114°$ 7 $a = 54°$, $b = 54°$, $c = 72°$
8 $x = y = 120°$ 9 $x = 10°$, $y = 140°$, $z = 30°$ 10 $a = 60°$, $b = 50°$, $c = 25°$
11 The triangles in **1**, **6**, **7** and **9** are congruent.

Exercise B
1 (a) $d = 6.40$ in (Pythagoras used), (b) angle $a = 38.7°$ (tan key used)
2 12 cm (you have to cut the rhombus into four identical triangles)
3 The height is 8.86 cm (sin key used). The area is 106 cm².

Exercise C
1 125°   2 135°   3 (a) 40°, (b) 140°   4 110°.

Chapter 13

The Use of Instruments

Essential Skills

(a) Ease with the protractor and a pair of compasses is assumed.
(b) Some knowledge of the angles of triangles is needed.

Basic Facts

The motto of this topic is that 'arcs earn marks!' The important skill when bisecting both lines and angles is the drawing of arcs.
Various triangles and quadrilaterals will be drawn.

Bisections

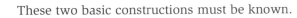

These two basic constructions must be known.

1. Bisection of an angle:

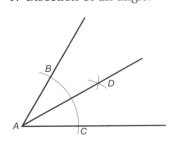   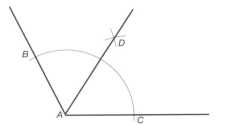

In both cases, the arc through B and C has centre A. The equal arcs at D come from B and C.

2. Bisecting a line:

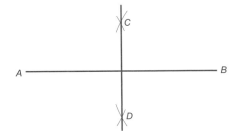

Two arcs are from A. Two arcs are from B. $AC = AD = BC = BD$.

Practise these skills. Draw any two angles and bisect them. Check your accuracy with a protractor. Draw any line and bisect it.

Constructing triangles

1   Construct a triangle *ABC* with *AB* = 7 cm, *AC* = 6 cm and *BC* = 5 cm. Measure angle *CAB*.

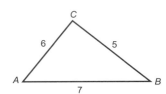

Make a rough sketch. It is easy to draw *AB*. The problem is to locate *C*. *C* is 6 cm from *A*; therefore, it is on a circle radius 6 cm centre *A*. Similarly, it is on a circle centre *B*, radius 5 cm.

Angle *CAB* = 44°.

Draw quite large arcs. It is good examination technique.

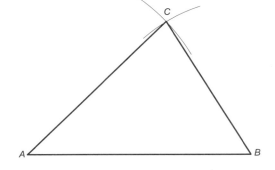

2   Construct a triangle *PQR* with *PQ* = 8 cm, angle *PQR* = 72° and angle *RPQ* = 51°. Measure the length of *PR*.

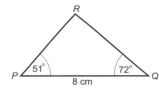

Make a rough sketch.

You may use your protractor as you have not been instructed otherwise.

PQ is easy to draw. *R* can be located by drawing both angles. *PR* is 9 cm.

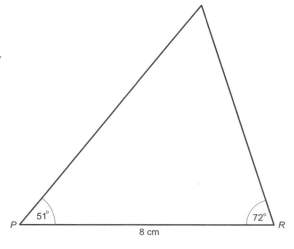

Constructing quadrilaterals

EXAMPLE

3

ABCD is a quadrilateral. *AB* = 45 mm, *AD* = 60 mm. *BD* = 50 mm, *BC* = 50 mm. *DC* = 50 mm.

Construct this quadrilateral. Measure and state the size of angle *ADC*.

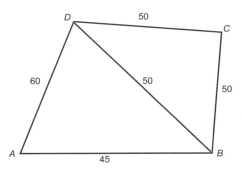

Make a rough sketch again. The rough sketch should help to decide:

(a) to draw *AB*
(b) to locate *D* using arcs
(c) to locate *C* using arcs.

Angle *ADC* = 107°.

The question is simply one of two triangles at the same time.

The importance of clear arcs cannot be over-stressed.

The locus of points

The constructions described earlier in the section headed bisections are used to solve two important locus problems.

Usually a locus is simply a path. It may be a straight line or a curve.

EXAMPLE

4

If you tie a brick on a piece of string and swing it around your head the locus of the brick will be a circle.

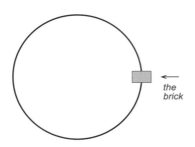

EXAMPLE

5

If you go for a stroll down a motorway making sure that you are always the same distance from the hard shoulder and the central reservation, you will be walking in a straight line.

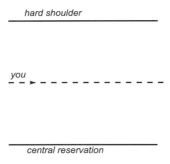

The following two standard constructions should be understood by all candidates.

(a) Find the locus of all points the same distance from two given points.

Let the points be *A* and *B*.

As all the points we are searching for are equidistant from *A* and *B* then they must lie on the line which bisects *AB* at right angles. We simply repeat construction 2 in the Bisection section.

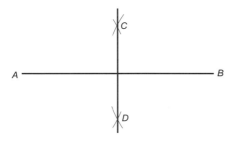

(b) Find the locus of all points the same distance from the two lines *AB* and *BC* in diagram (i):

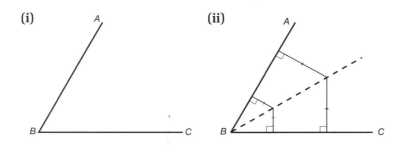

Common sense suggests that this locus is roughly as in diagram (ii). Further thought should make you realise that the locus is the angle bisector. So repeat bisection (i) as in diagram (iii).

(iii)

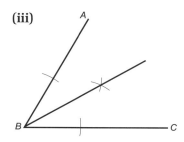

You should practise both of these constructions. They are often combined in examinations.

AMPLE

6

A triangle *ABC* has *AB* = 7 cm, *AC* = 8 cm and *BC* = 9 cm.
A point *x* is the same distance from *B* as from *C*. It is also the same distance from the lines *AC* and *BC*.
Draw the triangle.
Find and mark the point *x*.
Show all necessary arcs.

Construct the triangle by drawing suitable arcs from *B* to *C*.
Bisect the line *BC* (the same distance from *B* and *C*).
Bisect the angle *C* (the same distance from *BC* and *AC*).

All ten arcs are important.
Questions 2 and 3 in Exercise B test these skills.

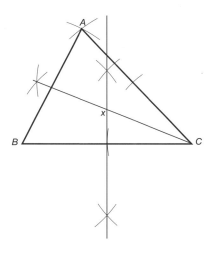

ERCISE

A

This exercise covers all the skills in this section.

1 Draw a line 5 cm long and bisect it.

2 Construct a triangle *XYZ* with *XY* = 8 cm, *XZ* = 6 cm and *YZ* = 7.5 cm. Measure angle *XYZ*.

3 Construct an equilateral triangle of side 7 cm using a ruler and compasses only.
Bisect angle *A*. Bisect the side *AC*. These bisectors meet at the point *D*. Measure *BD*.

4 Construct a quadrilateral *PQRS* with *PQ* = 8 cm, angle *SPQ* = 80°, angle *PQS* = 30°, *SR* = 7 cm and *RQ* = 6 cm. Measure angle *SRQ*.

EXERCISE

B

These three questions are of a more searching nature.

1 *ABC* is a triangle. *BC* = 9 cm, *AB* = 8 cm and *AC* = 7.5 cm. *D* is the point within the triangle *ABC* such that *AD* = *BD* and *D* is the same distance from the lines *AC* and *BC*.

Construct the triangle *ABC*. Find the point *D*. All necessary arcs must be shown.

2 *ABCD* is a quadrilateral. *AB* = 36 mm, *BC* = 48 mm, *CD* = 25 mm and *DA* = 65 mm. The length of the diagonal *AC* = 60 mm.

Construct the quadrilateral.

Bisect *AC*. Label the mid-point of *AC* by *M*. Draw a circle of centre *M* which passes through the points *A* and *C*.

3 A farmer's field *ABCD* is a rectangle *AB* = 80 m, *BC* = 60 m. There is a tap in this field. The tap is the same distance from *A* and *B*. It is the same distance from the sides *AB* and *BC*.

Choose a suitable scale and draw the field. Construct suitable loci and find and mark the tap *T*. Measure the length of *DT* to the nearest metre.

Answers

Exercise **A**   **2** Angle *XYZ* = 45°   **3** *BD* = 4 cm   **4** Angle *R* = 80°.

Exercise **B**   **1** To find *D*: (a) bisect the line *AB*; (b) bisect the angle *ACB*.
2 If your quadrilateral is accurate the circle should go through *B* as well. Angle *BAD* = 76°.
3 *DT* = 45 m.

Area

> ## Essential Skills
>
> (a) The ability to substitute into formulae would help (see Chapter 4).
>
> (b) You will need to have met the square root key and the π key.
>
> ## Basic Facts
>
> The area of a rectangle = length × breadth.
>
> The area of a triangle = $\dfrac{\text{base} \times \text{height}}{2}$.
>
> The area of a parallelogram = base × height.
>
> The area of a trapezium = $\frac{1}{2}(a+b) \times h$.
>
> The perimeter of any of these is the total distance around the edge.
>
> The area of a circle = πr^2.
>
> The circumference of a circle = πd or $2\pi r$.
>
> These two final formulae are never provided on examination reference sheets.

Some early examples

MPLES

1–4

1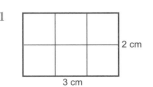

2 cm

3 cm

Find the area of this rectangle. It is 3 cm long and 2 cm wide.
Clearly its area = $3 \times 2 = 6 \, \text{cm}^2$.

2 (a) Find the areas of these two triangles.

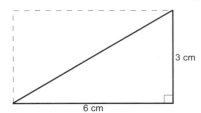

Every triangle is a half of a rectangle.

$$A = \frac{6 \times 3}{2} = 9 \text{ cm}^2.$$

(b)

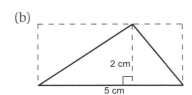

The matching rectangle is not obvious this time, but again the triangle is half a rectangle.

$$A = \frac{5 \times 2}{2} = 5 \text{ cm}^2.$$

3

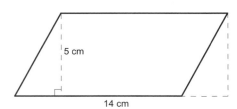

Find the area of this parallelogram. It is easily compared with a rectangle.

Area = base × height = $14 \times 5 = 70 \text{ cm}^2$.

4

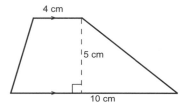

Find the area of this trapezium.

The formula $A = \frac{1}{2}(a + b)h$ is given to you. Use it! a and b are the parallel sides. h is the height.

$A = \frac{1}{2}(4 + 10) \times 5 = \frac{1}{2} \times 14 \times 5 = 35 \text{ cm}^2.$

EXERCISE

A

Find the area of the following.

1 A square of side 15 cm.

2 A triangle of base 7 cm and height 3 cm.

3 The shapes sketched below:

(a)

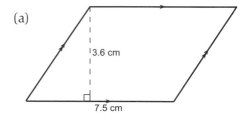

(b)

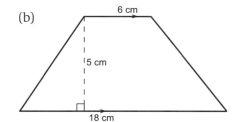

4 Find (a) the area and (b) the perimeter of a rectangle with a length of 8.4 cm and breadth of 2.5 cm. State the units of both your answers.

The reverse process

On occasions the area is given and one of the dimensions is not known. Normally when you are finding an area you end up multiplying two distances together. In this exercise we will be doing the reverse of this. The reverse of multiplying is dividing.

5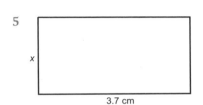

The area of this rectangle is 9.25 cm². Its length is 3.7 cm. Find its width (marked x).

$3.7 \times x = 9.25$
$\qquad x = 9.25 \div 3.7 = 2.5 \text{ cm}.$

6

The area of this parallelogram is 76.5 cm². Its height is 9 cm. Calculate the length of its base.

$9 \times b = 76.5$
$\qquad b = 76.5 \div 9 = 8.5 \text{ cm}.$

7

The area of this triangle is 102 cm². Its base is 17 cm. Calculate its height (marked h).

The given formula is $\dfrac{b \times h}{2} = A$.

Substituting in the numbers you get $\dfrac{17 \times h}{2} = 102$.

Cross multiplying $17h = 204$
$\qquad h = 204 \div 17 = 12 \text{ cm}.$

8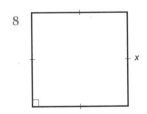

The area of this square is 60 m². Calculate its length x.

$x^2 = 60$. You must use the square root key.
$x = \sqrt{60} = 7.75 \text{ m (3 s.f.)}.$

1 The area of a square is 441 cm². Calculate its length.

2 The area of a rectangle 17.28 m². Its length is 4.8 m. Calculate its width.

3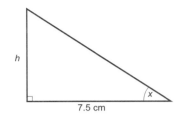

The area of this right angled triangle is 15 cm². (a) Calculate its height h. (b) Suggest methods to find: (i) the length of the third side; (ii) the angle marked x.

7.5 cm

Some problems

Sometimes the examiner combines two of the skills considered so far. Here are two examples.

9

14 m

25 m

4 m

4 m

This diagram illustrates a rectangular garden. It is mainly lawn but it contains a small square rose bed. Calculate (a) the area of the whole garden (b) the area of the rose bed (c) the lawn area.

(a) Whole garden: $25 \times 14 = 350 \, \text{m}^2$.
(b) Rose bed: $4 \times 4 = 16 \, \text{m}^2$.
(c) The lawn: $350 - 16 = 334 \, \text{m}^2$.

10 How many square tiles of length 50 cm would it take to cover a floor 6 m long and 4.5 m wide?

The units are mixed. You can either work totally in centimetres or in metres. This solution uses centimetres.
One row needs $600 \div 50 = 12$ tiles.
The number of rows would be $450 \div 50 = 9$.
You would need $12 \times 9 = 108$ tiles.

Try the two similar problems in Exercise C.

1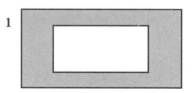

This diagram shows a picture which has been mounted on a piece of card. The picture is 14 cm by 9 cm. The card is 18 cm by 13 cm. Find the area of the border (shaded in the diagram).

2 Calculate the number of tiles, each 20 cm by 20 cm, that it would take to cover a floor of dimensions 3 m by 2 m.

The area of a circle

11 Find the area of a circle of radius 3 cm.

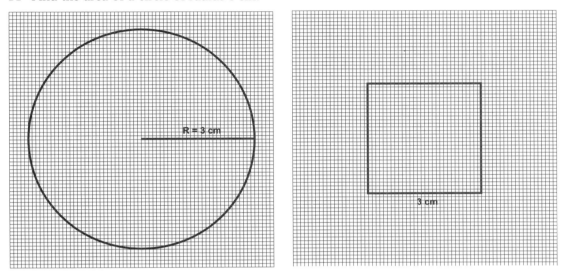

R = 3 cm

3 cm

Most attempts to prove that $A = \pi r^2$ (π is a Greek letter pronounced 'pie'), leave students unconvinced. The above diagrams illustrate:

   (i)   the required circle
   (ii) a square.

Clearly, the area of the square is $3 \times 3 = 9$ cm^2.
The area of the circle is $\pi \times 3 \times 3$.
Using the π button on your calculator, $\pi \times 3 \times 3 = 28.3$ cm^2 (3 s.f.).
The diagrams are provided simply to convince you that the formula is a reasonable one. The circle is about three times bigger than the square, isn't it? (Count the little squares, if you like.)

12 Find the area of a circle of radius 10 cm.

$$A = \pi r^2$$
$$= \pi \times 10 \times 10$$
$$= 314 \text{ cm}^2 \text{ (3 s.f.)}.$$

13 A circular flower bed has a diameter of 12 ft. Find its area.

Do not be put off by the use of imperial units.
Notice that it is the radius we use.

$$D = 12 \text{ ft}$$
$$R = 6 \text{ ft}$$
$$A = \pi r^2 = \pi \times 6^2$$
$$= \pi \times 36$$
$$= 113 \text{ ft}^2.$$

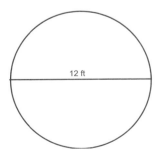

12 ft

---

14 Find the radius of a circle if its area is 140 cm². (This reverse method needs more thought.)

$$\pi r^2 = 140 \quad \text{(divide by } \pi\text{)}$$
$$r^2 = \frac{140}{\pi} = 44.56 \quad \text{(using the } \pi \text{ key)}$$
$$r = \sqrt{44.56}$$
$$= 6.68 \text{ cm} \quad \text{(3 s.f.)}.$$

15 Find the diameter of a circle of area 100 cm².

First, we need the radius. Again,

$$\pi r^2 = 100$$
$$\text{and } r^2 = \frac{100}{\pi} = 31.83$$
$$r = \sqrt{31.83} = 5.642$$
$$D = 2 \times r$$
$$= 11.3 \text{ m (3 s.f.)}.$$

EXERCISE

D

Give the answers to 3 s.f. in the following.

1 Find the area of a circle if its radius is 9 cm.
2 Find the area of a circle of diameter 50 m.
3 The circle at the centre of a soccer pitch has a diameter of 10 yd. Find the area of this circle.
4 A circular ring has an area of 6 m². Find the radius of this ring.
5 A circular mirror has an area of 200 cm². Find its diameter.

The circumference

The perimeter of this square is 4 × 4 cm or 16 cm. A reasonable guess at the perimeter of the circle would be 3 × 4 (or 3× diameter). The perimeter of a circle is called its circumference. The formula for the circumference can be shown to be $C = \pi \times D$ or πD.

This diagram only illustrates that this is a reasonable result. As the diameter is twice the radius, or $D = 2r$, clearly $\pi \times 2r$ or $2\pi r$ is another acceptable formula.

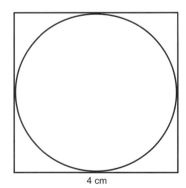

4 cm

16 Find the circumference of a circle of diameter 30 cm.

(A quick estimate is $3 \times 30 = 90$ cm.)

You write: $C = \pi D$

$\qquad = \pi \times 30$

$\qquad = 94.2$ cm.

17 The radius of a circle if 4 m. Find its circumference using $\pi = 3.1$.

$C = 2 \times \pi \times r$

$\qquad = 2 \times 3.1 \times 4$

$\qquad = 24.8$ m.

18 The circumference of a circle is 32 miles. Find its diameter.

$\pi \times D = 32$

therefore $D = \dfrac{32}{\pi}$

$\qquad = 10.2$ miles.

19 Find the radius of a circle of circumference 60 cm.

Either $\pi \times D = 60$ $\qquad$ or $\qquad$ $2\pi r = 60$

$\qquad D = \dfrac{60}{\pi}$ $\qquad\qquad\qquad\qquad r = \dfrac{60}{2\pi}$

$\qquad\quad = 19.10$ cm

$\qquad r = \dfrac{19.10}{2}$

$\qquad\quad = 9.55$ cm $\qquad\qquad\qquad\qquad = 9.55$ cm.

Try these.

1 Find the circumference (to 3 s.f.) of the steering wheel of a car if the steering wheel's diameter is 32 cm.

2 The length of the minute hand of a watch is 2 cm. How far does the point of the hand travel in 1 h?

3 Find the diameter of a circle of circumference 75 cm.

4 Use $\pi = 3$ to estimate the radius of a circle of circumference 42 cm.

Chapter 14

Some applications

20 Find the area of the shaded ring. The radius of the larger circle is 5 cm. The small radius is 3 cm.

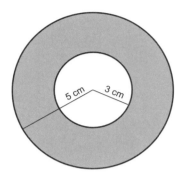

Area of large circle: $\pi \times 5^2$ $= 78.54$ cm^2.
Area of small circle: $\pi \times 3^2$ $= 28.27$ cm^2.
Area of ring: $78.54 - 28.27$ $= 50.3$ cm^2 (3 s.f.)

21

90 m

70 m

The diagram above is of a running track. Calculate the total area enclosed by its shape. The shape is a rectangle and two semicircles, i.e. a rectangle and a whole circle.

Area of rectangle $= 90 \times 70 = 6300$ m^2.
Are of circle $= \pi r^2 = \pi \times 35 \times 35 = 3848$ cm^2.
Total area $= 10\,148$ m^2
                 $= 10\,100$ m^2 (to 3 s.f.).

22 The tyre of a car has a diameter of 34 cm. How far in kilometres does the car travel if the wheel rotates 2500 times?

1 revolution $= \pi \times D = 106.8$ cm
2500 revolutions $= 106.8 \times 2500 = 267\,000$
                 $= 2.67$ km.   ($\div 100\,000$)
(As 100 cm $= 1$ m and 1000 m $= 1$ km, so 100 000 cm $= 1$ km.)

23 Find the perimeter of the shape in question 21 above.

The perimeter has four parts:

   two straight edges of 90 m $\rightarrow$ 180 m
   two semicircles $\rightarrow$ one circle.

Length of circumference of circle $= \pi \times D = \pi \times 70$ m $= 219.9$ m.
Whole perimeter $= 400$ m (3 s.f.).

Try these.

1 A circle of radius 6 cm was inscribed in a square of side 12 cm. Calculate the total area of those parts of the square which are outside the circle (shaded in the diagram).

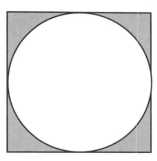

2 Find the area of the ring in this diagram.

$$R = 10 \text{ ft}$$
$$r = 6 \text{ ft.}$$

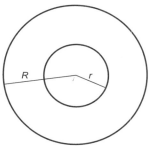

3 A marble of radius 1.5 cm rolled a total distance of 27 m. How many revolutions did it make?

4 Find the perimeter of a semicircle of radius 8 cm.

Answers

Exercise A   **1** 225 cm²   **2** 10.5 cm²   **3** (a) 27 cm², (b) 60 cm²   **4** (a) 21 cm², (b) 21.8 cm.

Exercise B   **1** 21 cm   **2** 3.6 cm   **3** (a) 4 cm, (b) (i) Pythagoras' theorem, (ii) trigonometry.

Exercise C   **1** 108 cm²   **2** 150 tiles.

Exercise D   **1** 254 cm²   **2** 1960 m²   **3** 78.5 yd²   **4** 1.38 m   **5** 16.0 cm.

Exercise E   **1** 101 cm   **2** 12.6 cm   **3** 23.9 cm   **4** 7 cm.

Exercise F   **1** 30.9 cm²   **2** 210 ft²   **3** 286 revolutions   **4** 41.1 cm (25.1+16).

Chapter 15

Volume and Surface Area of Solids

Essential Skills

The recognition and the vocabulary of solids, including cuboid, cube, cylinder, prism, pyramid, vertices, faces and edges.

Basic Facts

The volume of any prism is given by:

    volume = area of cross section × height.

Thus, the volume of a cuboid is:

    volume = length × breadth × height.

For a cylinder:

    volume = πr^2 × height.

Prisms and pyramids

A prism is a solid figure with an unchanging cross-section. Each one usually takes its name from its cross-section.

The Egyptians made the word 'pyramid' a household one. Pyramids, in general, are of the 'Egyptian' shape, but the bases are not always squares. Pyramids take their names from the shapes of their bases.

Here are sketches of four common prisms and three common pyramids.

Prisms:

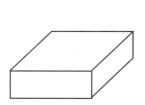 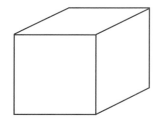 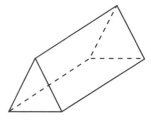

rectangular prism (cuboid, or 'box')

circular prism (cylinder)

square prism (cube)

triangular prism

Pyramids:

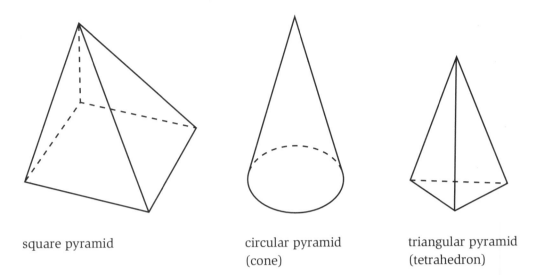

square pyramid

circular pyramid
(cone)

triangular pyramid
(tetrahedron)

Of course, these shapes are much more commonly known by the names in brackets, but the definition of how these solids take their names is still valid.

In school, we usually make models of these shapes from card. We do so by imagining the solids' faces laid flat. When the faces are laid flat the resulting shape is called the *net*. Here are seven possible nets of the shapes sketched earlier. They are out of order; which is which?

(a)

(b)

(c)

(d)

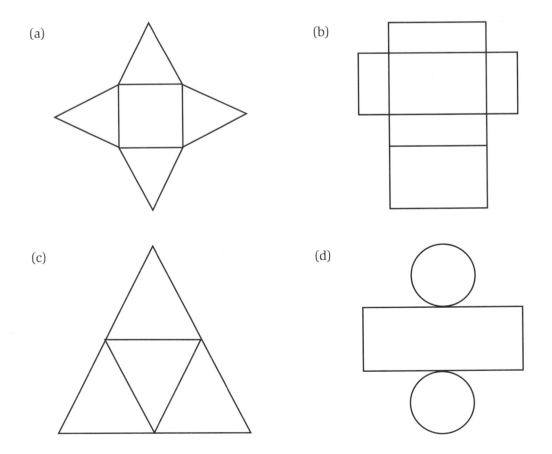

(e)

(f)

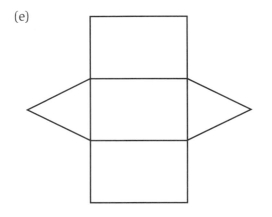

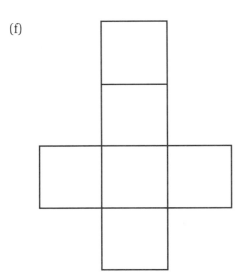

(g)

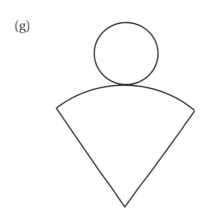

They are: (a) square pyramid
(b) cuboid
(c) triangular pyramid
(d) cylinder
(e) triangular prism
(f) cube
(g) cone.

An understanding of nets will help a great deal when surface areas are considered.

The cuboid

This is a common shape. You are probably surrounded by them. Are you reading this while eating breakfast? The muesli box is a cuboid. Why not tear it apart to check its net and count its vertices?

The volume of any prism = cross-sectional area × height.
This is easy to illustrate in the case of a cuboid.

Chapter 15

1   Find the volume of this cuboid.

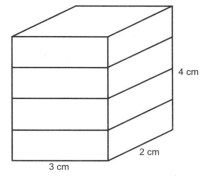

$$V = L \times B \times H$$
$$= 3 \times 2 \times 4$$
$$= 24 \text{ cm}^3.$$

This is why.

Each layer is a cross
section like this:

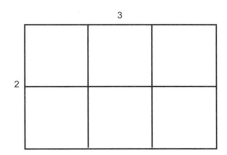

There are four layers:

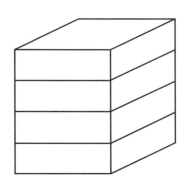

Clearly, one layer of cubes $(3 \times 2 = 6) = 6 \text{ cm}^3$.
Each layer is identical, so $V = 6 \times 4 = 24 \text{ cm}^3$.

2   Calculate the volume of a cube of side 7 cm.

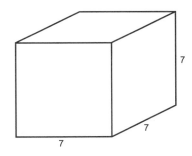

$$V = 7 \times 7 \times 7 \quad (\text{or } 7^3)$$
$$= 343 \text{ cm}^3.$$

3   A cuboid's volume is 150 in^3. Its base is a square of side 5 in. Find its height.

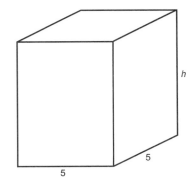

Let the height be h:
$$5 \times 5 \times h = 150$$
$$25h = 150$$
$$h = 6 \text{ in.}$$

4   The volume of a cube is 512 cm^3. Find the length of an edge.

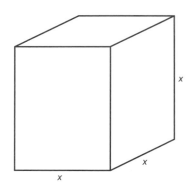

Let the length be x:
$$x \times x \times x = 512$$
$$x^3 = 512$$
$$x = \sqrt[3]{512}$$
$$x = 8 \text{ cm}.$$

The cube root, in this case, can be found by trial and error. Most scientific calculators will provide this answer.

5   Find the total surface area of the cuboid in this diagram. The dimensions are in centimetres.

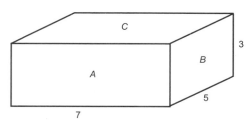

There are six faces, all rectangles. There are three sizes of rectangle, two of each size. The net illustrates this.

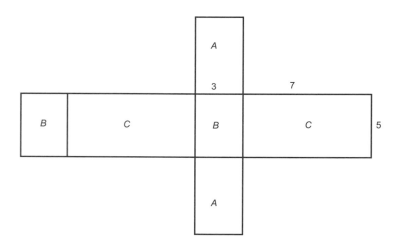

Therefore, the total surface area is:
C: $2 \times 7 \times 5 = 70$ cm^2
B: $2 \times 5 \times 3 = 30$ cm^2
A: $2 \times 7 \times 3 = 42$ cm^2.

Total surface area = 142 cm^2.

6   Find the total surface area of a cube of side 13 cm.

The six faces are identical this time:
area of one face $= 13 \times 13$ (or 13^2) $= 169$ cm^2
total surface area $= 169 \times 6$ $= 1014$ cm^2.

ERCISE

A

Try these six questions.

1   Find the volume of a cuboid of length 5 m, breadth 4 m and height 2.5 m.
2   The volume of a box is 210 cm^3. Its height is 5 cm and its breadth 6 cm. Find its length.
3   Find the volume of a cube of side 5 in.
4   The total surface area of a cube is 600 cm^2. Find the length of an edge.
5   Find the total surface area of a cuboid which measures 9 cm long by 6 cm by 4 cm.
6   The volume of a cube is 64 cm^3. Find the length of an edge.

The volume of cylinders and other prisms

A cylinder is also a very common shape, especially in the kitchen. Vegetables, soup and fruit are all sold in cans which are cylinders.

The volume of any prism is the area of cross-section $\times$ height, as each layer has the same volume; so the argument is much as that used for the simple box earlier in this chapter. The shape of the cross-section does not matter.

MPLES

–10

7   Find the volume of a cylinder of radius 6 cm and height 10 cm.

The shape is a prism, and the area of the cross-section is πr^2.
Therefore the volume $= \pi r^2 h$
$$V = \pi \times 6^2 \times 10$$
$$= 1130 \text{ cm}^3 \text{ (3 s.f.)}.$$

8   The area of the cross-section of a prism is 40 cm^2. Its height is 9 cm. Find its volume.

The shape is immaterial:
the volume $=$ cross-sectional area $\times$ height
$$= 40 \times 9$$
$$= 360 \text{ cm}^3.$$

9   A petrol tank is cylindrical. Its internal dimensions are a radius of 30 cm and a height of 90 cm. Calculate:

(a) its capacity in cm^3
(b) its capacity in litres (1000 cm^3 = 1 litre).

(a)
$$V = \pi r^2 h$$
$$= \pi \times 30^2 \times 90$$
$$= 254\,000 \text{ cm}^3 \qquad \text{(3 s.f.)}.$$
(b)
$$V = 254 \text{ litres} \qquad (\div 1000).$$

10 This triangle is the cross-section of a triangular prism of height 20 cm. Find its volume.

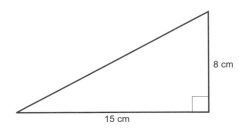

Again, as it is a prism: V = base area × height.
The area of a triangle $= \frac{b \times h}{2}$
$$= \frac{15 \times 8}{2}$$
$$= 60 \text{ cm}^2.$$
The volume of the prism $= 60 \times 20$
$$= 1200 \text{ cm}^3.$$

EXERCISE B

Find the volumes of these.

1 A cylinder of radius 3 cm and height 10 cm.
2 A prism with a cross-sectional area of 10 m^2 and height 3 m.
3 A cylindrical can of radius 8 cm and height 25 cm.
4 A prism with this trapezium as its cross-section and a height of 20 cm.

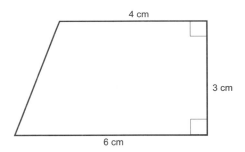

EXERCISE C

1 Find the volume of a box of dimensions 13 in by 10 in by 6 in.

2 Find the total surface of a cube of side 8 cm.

3 Find the volume (to 3 s.f.) of a cylinder of radius 10 cm and height 6 cm.

4 The volume of a prism is 120 cm^3. Its height is 8 cm. Find the area of its cross-section.

5 A cuboid has a volume of 720 cm^3. Its height is 12 cm and its length is 10 cm. Find its breadth.

6   A large cylinder of radius 8 cm and height 12 cm is full of perfume. Its contents are poured into small bottles; each bottle contained 20 ml. Find:

   (a) the volume of the cylinder;
   (b) the number of bottles which can be filled.

7   A cube and a cylinder are of equal volume. The cylinder's radius is 5 cm and its height is 12 cm. Find:

   (a) the cylinder's volume;
   (b) the length of the edge of the cube.

Answers

ercise A   **1** 50 cm³   **2** 7 cm   **3** 125 in³   **4** 10 cm   **5** 228 cm²   **6** 4 cm

ercise B   **1** 283 cm³ (3 s.f.)   **2** 30 m³   **3** 5030 cm³ (3 s.f.)   **4** 300 cm³

ercise C   **1** 780 in³   **2** 384 cm²   **3** 1880 cm² (3 s.f.)   **4** 15 cm²   **5** 6 cm
   6 (a) 2413 cm³, (b) 120 (not 121!)   **7** (a) 942.5 cm³, (b) 9.80 cm (3 s.f.) cube root key must be used here.

Chapter 16

Transformations

Essential Skills

(a) Some basic knowledge of symmetry would help.
(b) You will need to be able to plot points on graph paper.
(c) Some simple knowledge of angles is necessary, e.g. right angles.

Basic Facts

There are two types of symmetry: line and rotational.
Four types of transformation will be met; they are (i) reflections (ii) rotations
(iii) translations and (iv) enlargements.

Symmetry

Line symmetry

If a shape has line symmetry it will fold along a straight line in such a way that one half will fit onto the other. Here are some examples.

An isosceles triangle   A rectangle   A regular hexagon

  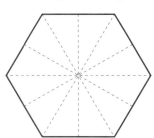

The dotted lines are the folds. Each is called an axis of symmetry. You can see that the number of axes can vary. You are often asked to count them. This triangle has one. The rectangle has two and this hexagon has six.

It is worth noting that a regular shape has the same number of axes as sides or angles; e.g. a square has four; an equilateral triangle has three; the regular hexagon above has six.

Rotational symmetry

If a shape can be turned about a central point to a new position which looks identical to the original position then it is said to have rotational symmetry. Here are two examples.

1 ABCD is a parallelogram with central point E which is where its diagonals cross.

When it is rotated through 180° about E it looks like this:

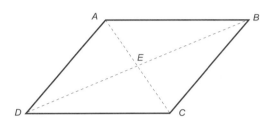 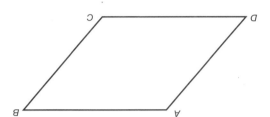

It looks the same. There are only two positions where it looks the same. It is said to have rotational symmetry with order two.

2 Here is a square   Here it is after   Here it is after   Here it is after
   ABCD   a rotation of   a rotation of   a rotation of 90°
                    90° clockwise.   180° clockwise.   anticlockwise

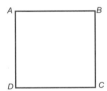 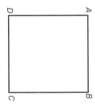 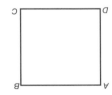

It has rotational symmetry with order four.

Regular shapes have the same order as their number of sides.

Reflections

When a shape is to be reflected a mirror line will be given. Each point of the original shape is moved so that its image is the same distance 'behind' the mirror that it was in 'front' of the mirror at first.

EXAMPLES

3–4

3 This question mark has been reflected in the vertical line *AB*.

4 This trapezium has been reflected in the horizontal line *CD*.

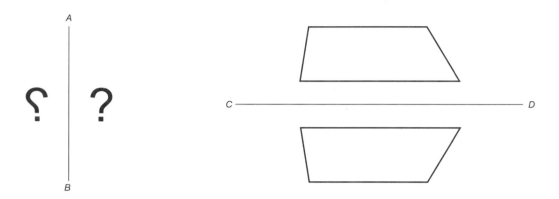

Occasionally the examiner will do the reflection for you. He will ask you for a full description. He expects you to use the word reflection and to state the position of the mirror line.

Rotations

When a shape is rotated about a point each part of the shape moves the same number of degrees about the point and stays the same distance from that point. The movement can be clockwise or anticlockwise. Here are two examples:

This rectangle has been rotated 90° about the point marked *X*.

This semicircle (A) has been rotated through 180° about (0,0) to the position labelled B.

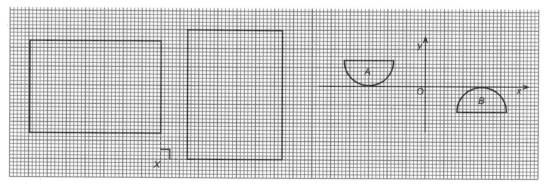

If the rotation is done for you then a full description must contain four points. They are (i) the word rotation (ii) the angle rotated (iii) the nature (clockwise or anticlockwise) and (iv) the centre of rotation.

Translations

A translation moves every point making up the shape in the same direction and for the same distance. Again here are two examples:

(i)   (ii)

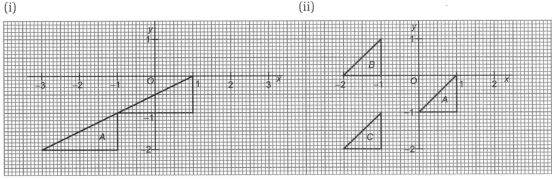

Triangle A has moved two units to the right and one unit up.

This sketch translates triangle A onto B. It is two to the left and one up. A onto C is two to the left and one down.

These movements can be written formally using vectors.

For (i) we say A maps onto B by the vector $\binom{2}{1}$. Note $\binom{x}{y}$ not $\binom{y}{x}$.

In (ii) A onto B is $\binom{-2}{1}$, i.e. movements to the left are negative. In (ii) A onto C is $\binom{-2}{-1}$, i.e. movements down are negative as well.

Any description must contain the word translation and the matching vector or equivalent.

Enlargements

Objects are enlarged and their images found after two pieces of information are provided:

(a) the scale factor is stated;

(b) the centre of enlargement is given.

5   Sketch the image of trapezium *ABCD* in the diagram. The scale factor is 2. The centre of enlargement is the point *P*.

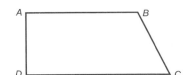

P.

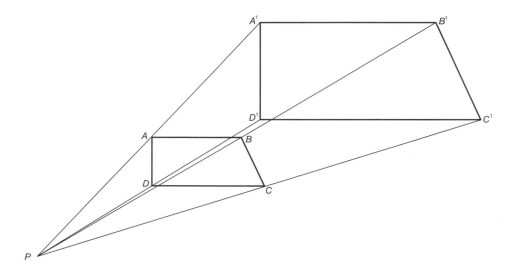

The solution is:

Draw straight lines through *PA, PB, PC* and *PD*.

Measure carefully so that $PA^1 = 2 \times PA$
$$PB^1 = 2 \times PB$$
$$PC^1 = 2 \times PC$$
and $PD^1 = 2 \times PD$.

The second trapezium is the same shape as the original one. They are said to be similar.

6   Sketch the image of the triangle *XYZ* below, after an enlargement scale factor $\frac{1}{2}$, using *A* as

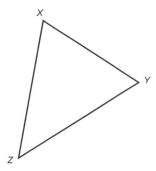

A•

the centre of enlargement.

The method is similar.

Join *AX, AY* and *AZ*. Measure carefully, so that this time:

$AX^1 = \frac{1}{2}$ of *AX*
$AY^1 = \frac{1}{2}$ of *AY*

Chapter 16

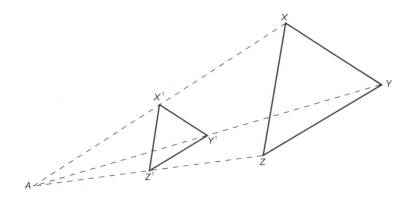

$AZ^1 = \frac{1}{2}$ of AZ.

The image is again similar to the object.

ERCISE

A

Try these two questions.

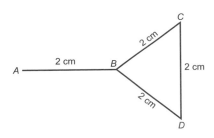

1   Copy this diagram.
    Draw the image of triangle *BCD* after an enlargement scale factor of 3, using *A* as the centre
    of the enlargement.

2   Copy the graph below. Draw the image of the triangle *ABC* after an enlargement scale factor
    $\frac{1}{2}$ and centre of enlargement *O*.

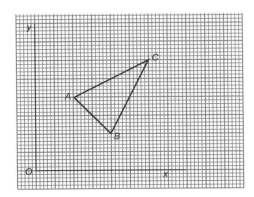

EXERCISE

B

1 Consider the five triangles given below.
  Describe in geometric terms the four transformations which map:
  (a) A onto B
  (b) A onto C
  (c) A onto E
  (d) A onto D.

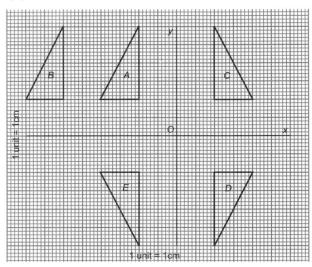

2 Copy these shapes and reflect each one in the line stated:
  (a) in the line *AC*   (b) in the line *PQ*.

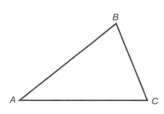
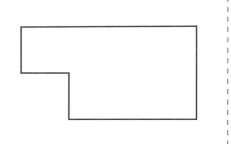

3 Copy this right angled triangle four times:

  (a) reflect it in the line *AC*
  (b) reflect it in the line *AB*
  (c) reflect it in the line *BC*
  (d) rotate it through 180° about the mid point of *AC*
  (e) give the full names of your four shapes.

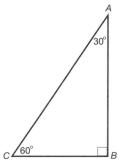

4 On graph paper plot the triangle with co-ordinates (1, 1), (1, 2) and (3, 1).
  (a) Rotate this triangle through 90° clockwise about the origin (0, 0) and plot its vertices.
  (b) Now rotate your original triangle 90° anticlockwise about (0, 0) and again plot the image. Write down the co-ordinates of your vertices in each case.

5 Consider these six geometrical shapes: a parallelogram, a rhombus, a kite, a rectangle, a scalene triangle and a regular pentagon.
  (a) Which of these shapes has (i) line symmetry only? (ii) rotational symmetry only? (iii) line and rotational symmetry? (iv) no symmetry?
  (b) Which has two lines of symmetry and has order of rotational symmetry 2?
  (c) Which simply has only one line of symmetry?
  (d) Which simply has order of rotational symmetry 2?
  (e) Which of them has five lines of symmetry and order of rotational symmetry 5?

Answers

Exercise A **1** You can check your answer with a ruler. The triangle should have sides of 6 cm. If you measure from *A* to your 'new' *C*, it should be about 11.2 cm long.
  2 Measure the sides of your new triangle. One should be about 0.7 cm. The other two should be both about 1.1 cm.

Exercise B **1** (a) A translation of $\begin{pmatrix} -2 \\ 0 \end{pmatrix}$ (b) a reflection in the *y* axis   (c) a reflection in the *x* axis
  (d) A rotation of 180° about (0, 0).
  2 (a) Your shape should be a kite   (b) the shape should now be 'pointing' to the right.
  3 In this order: a kite, an equilateral triangle, an isosceles triangle, a rectangle.
  4 (a) The vertices are (1, −1), (1, −3) and (2, −1)
   (b) The vertices are (−1, 1), (−2, 1) and (−1, 3).
  5 (a) (i) the kite, (ii) the parallelogram, (iii) rhombus, rectangle and the regular pentagon,
     (iv) the scalene triangle
   (b) the rectangle and the rhombus
   (c) the kite
   (d) the parallelogram
   (e) the regular pentagon.

Trigonometry, Pythagoras' Theorem and Similar Triangles

Essential Skills

You need to have mastered the following:

(a) the use of the following keys on your scientific calculator:
   (i)   the **square root**;
   (ii) **sin**, **cos** and **tan**;
   (iii) **second function**, sometimes called **shift** or **inverse**;
   (iv) the **fraction key** (optional here).

If you are unsure, consult the instructions that came with your calculator (if you haven't thrown them away), or ask your brother or sister or nag your teacher.

(b) Solving equations by cross multiplying (see Chapter 5).

Basic Facts

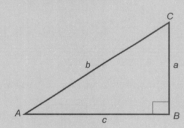

$$\left.\begin{array}{l} a^2 = b^2 - c^2 \\ c^2 = b^2 - a^2 \\ b^2 = a^2 + c^2 \end{array}\right\}$$ Pythagoras' theorem.

For angle A: a is opposite; c is adjacent; b is the hypotenuse.

$$\sin A = \frac{a}{b} = \frac{\text{opposite}}{\text{hypotenuse}} \qquad \cos A = \frac{c}{b} = \frac{\text{adjacent}}{\text{hypotenuse}} \qquad \tan A = \frac{a}{c} = \frac{\text{opposite}}{\text{adjacent}}$$

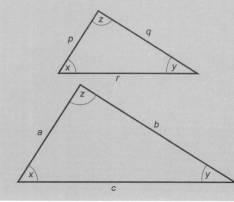

As these triangles are the same shape there is a fixed scale.

So $\dfrac{p}{a} = \dfrac{q}{b} = \dfrac{r}{c}$.

These eight examples should make the facts clearer.

1   Calculate the length of *AB*.

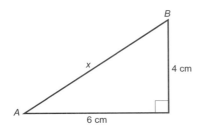

Your thoughts should be:

the problem is about **three** sides. This must be Pythagoras' theorem. *AB* is the longest side. I must add the squares.

Let $AB = x$, $x^2 = 4^2 + 6^2$
                     $x^2 = 52$
                       $x = 7.21$ cm.

2   Calculate the length of *PR*.

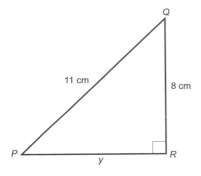

This is three sides again. This time we need one of the shorter sides. *y* is clearly less than 11 cm. You must subtract squares.

$y^2 = 11^2 - 8^2$
$y^2 = 57$
  $y = 7.55$ cm.

3   Calculate *x* to 1 d.p.

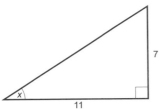

Your thoughts should be:

'It's trigonometry', 7 is opposite, 11 is adjacent. It is a tangent problem.

You write: $\tan x = \dfrac{7}{11}$

$x = 32.5°$

Calculator: either $7 \div 11 =$
              or $7\ \mathbf{a}^{\mathbf{b}}/_{\mathbf{c}}\ 11$
using second function.

4   Calculate *y*.

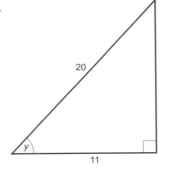

11 is adjacent, 20 is hypotenuse.

$\cos y = \dfrac{11}{20}$

$y = 56.6°.$

5   Calculate the length of *AB*.

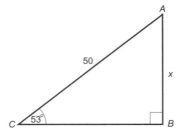

Only one side is known. It must be trigonometry.

x is opposite; 50 is hypotenuse.

$$\sin 53° = \frac{x}{50} \qquad \text{cross multiply}$$

$$x = 50 \times \sin 53°$$
$$x = 39.9 \text{ cm.}$$

6   Find the length of *AB*.

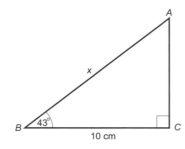

AB is the hypotenuse, *BC* is adjacent, therefore cos.

Let *AB* = *x*

$$\cos 43° = \frac{10}{x} \qquad \text{cross multiply}$$

$$x \times \cos 43° = 10$$

$$x = \frac{10}{\cos 43°}$$

$$x = 13.7 \text{ cm.}$$

7   These triangles are the same shape. There is a fixed scale. Match the sides.

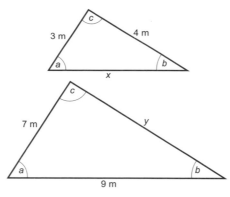

The scale is $\dfrac{3}{7}$ or $\dfrac{4}{y}$ or $\dfrac{x}{9}$;

$\dfrac{3}{7}$ is the critical one.

Therefore: $\dfrac{3}{7} = \dfrac{4}{y}$ $\dfrac{3}{7} = \dfrac{x}{9}.$

Cross multiplying: $3y = 28$ $7x = 27$
                                      $y = 9.33$ cm $x = 3.86$ cm.

8   All units are in centimetres. *AB* is parallel to *DE*.
Find the lengths of *x* and *y*.

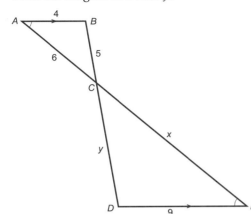

Because of the parallel lines:

$A = E$ z angles   5 matches *y*
$B = D$ z angles   6 matches *x*
$C = C$ x angles   4 matches 9.

The scale is $\dfrac{4}{9}$:

$$\dfrac{4}{9} = \dfrac{6}{x}$$

$$4x = 54$$
$$x = 13.5 \text{ cm}$$

$$\dfrac{4}{9} = \dfrac{5}{y}$$

$$4y = 45$$
$$y = 11.25 \text{ cm.}$$

Try these questions.

1   Calculate the length of the distances marked *x* and *y*.

(a)

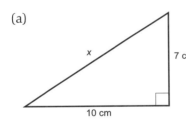

(b)

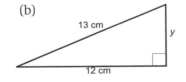

2   Calculate angle *ABC*.

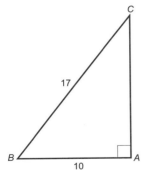

3 Calculate the lengths of x and y.

(a)

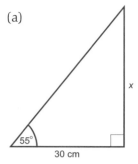

(b)

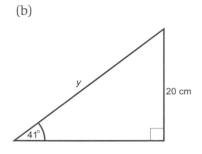

4 Use similar triangles to calculate the lengths p and q.

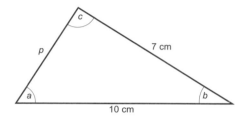

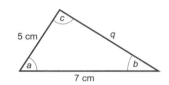

5 All units are centimetres.
(a) Use trigonometry to find a.
(b) Use Pythagoras' theorem to find the length of x.
(c) Use similar triangles to find the lengths of y and z.

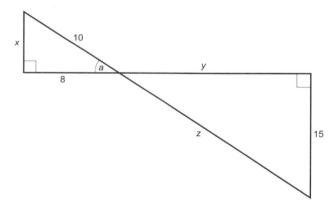

Answers

Exercise **A**

1 (a) $x = 12.2$ (b) $y = 5$

2 $54.0°$

3 (a) 42.8 cm   (b) 30.5 cm

4 $p = 7.14$ cm, $q = 4.9$ cm

5 $a = 36.9°$, $x = 6$ cm, $y = 20$ cm, $z = 25$ cm.

Chapter 18

The Collection and Display of Statistics

Essential Skills

This first section about statistics covers the early skills. Very little is assumed.

Basic Facts

Data are collected in this way:

Group	Tally	f	
1–5	⊦⊦⊦⊦ ||	7	etc.

Several simple diagrams can be used to display data, including:

(a) bar charts

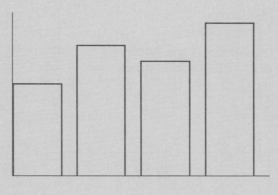

(b) pictograms

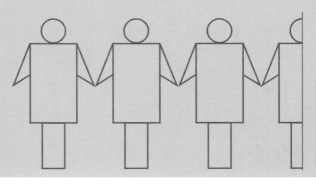

Collection

In statistics we must handle numbers for various reasons. However, whatever our intentions we must collect this information first.

1   Here are the results of a spelling test which was taken by 25 pupils. The maximum mark was 5.

1	3	2	4	3
3	2	2	4	3
2	3	3	2	3
2	4	4	5	3
3	3	4	2	1

This jumble of numbers needs to be put in order. A table (as below), called a frequency table, is a way of sorting the numbers. Work across each row. Put a single tally stroke '|' for each number. To make the final adding easy, use each fifth stroke to cross the other four, like this: 卌. Here is the frequency table of the test results above.

Score	Tally	Freq. (f)
1	||	2
2	卌 ||	7
3	卌 卌	10
4	卌	5
5	|	1
Total	(a useful check)	**25**

If the marks had been more spread out, we may have wanted to put them into *groups*.

2   Here are the ages of 30 people who attended a pop concert:

16	8	18	20	17	6	21	28	12	17
11	18	18	23	15	16	13	19	22	16
17	21	14	24	14	13	17	16	19	9

The ages range from 6 to 28. Groups of 1–5, 6–10, 11–15, etc. have been chosen. The table looks like this:

Age	Tally	Freq. (f)
1–5		0
6–10	|||	3
11–15	卌 ||	7
16–20	卌 卌 ||||	14
21–25	卌	5
26–30	|	1
Total	(checking again)	**30**

1   40 people were asked to choose their favourite comedy T.V. programme from the following:
    A   *Men Behaving Badly*
    B   *Friends*
    C   *Frasier*
    D   *Have I Got News For You*
    E   *Third Rock from the Sun*

Their responses were:

A	D	C	B	E	E	B	A	D	C
C	D	B	B	E	A	E	A	B	B
C	B	B	E	E	A	B	B	A	B
A	E	E	B	B	A	C	D	B	C

Draw up a table of their choices.

2   Here are the mathematics results of 48 G.C.S.E. students. The maximum mark was 50. Draw up a table of these results using groups 1–10, 11–20, 21–30, etc.

12	23	31	46	42	46	48	29
27	31	26	38	7	28	36	43
19	27	24	31	36	11	44	50
19	28	31	34	22	27	36	5
27	33	41	17	28	26	19	31
32	41	40	9	36	28	32	27

Bar graphs

The bar graph below illustrates the favourite interests of some adults:

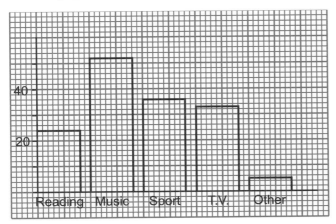

The vertical scale is the most important one. Check that you can 'read' a small square. In this case, as five small squares represent ten adults, then one small square represents two adults.

EXAMPLE

3

Use the bar graph above to answer the following questions.

(a) What is the most popular hobby?
(b) How many chose sport?
(c) How many more adults chose T.V. than reading?
(d) What is the total number of adults represented in the diagram?

(a) Music (the highest column).
(b) 36 (33 would be a common error).
(c) 33 − 24 = 9.
(d) 24 + 52 + 36 + 33 + 5 = 150.

EXERCICE

B

1   A mock election was held in a high school and the way in which the sixth-formers voted was noted on the graph below. Use this graph to answer the following questions.

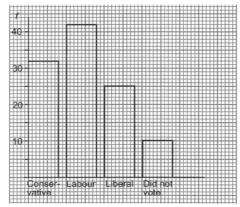

(a) How many people are represented by one small square on the vertical axis?
(b) How many voted Liberal Democrat?
(c) How many more people voted Labour than Liberal Democrat?
(d) How many sixth-formers voted?

2   Draw a bar graph to illustrate the following information.

The monthly T.V. viewing (in hours) of an average adult is:

serials	34 h
sport	21 h
documentaries & news	17 h
comedy programmes	13 h
others	9 h.

3   The following vehicles passed a school in 30 min:

cars	48
buses	6
bicycles	7
lorries & vans	29
motorcycles	16.

Illustrate this information with a bar chart.

Pictograms

If a bar chart is to be shown on television, or is to be printed in a newspaper, it is often dressed up so that each column (which is simply a rectangle) becomes a shape linked to the information given.

E.g.   if the size of families is being depicted,
          3 units become three children
or: if it is the sale of milk,
          5 units become five milk bottles, etc.

The pets of some young children were first drawn as a block graph:

And then the same information was displayed as a pictogram.

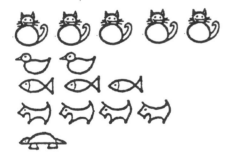

1   Design suitable symbols to illustrate:

(a) the various forms of transport used by people to get to work;
(b) the types of house inhabited by people in a town, e.g. flats, detached houses, etc.;
(c) the favourite hobbies of the adults in the earlier question, i.e. music, sport, T.V. and reading.

2   Draw a pictogram, using your symbols, for question 1(c) if the figures are:

          music   25
          sport   30
          T.V.   12
          reading   16.

Your attempt at question 2 above will bring home to you the main problems. For example, if you let one T.V. set represent five adults, you will have had the problem of showing 12 adults. 'Two and a bit' T.V. sets is too vague.

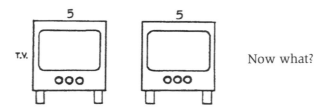

Now what?

A *good* pictogram is supposed to give numerical facts as well as being interesting.

Answers

Exercise A   1 A = 8, B = 14, C = 6, D = 4 and E = 8
                 2 1–10: 3   11–20: 6   21–30: 15   31–40: 15   41–50: 9.

Exercise B   1 (a) 1   (b) 25   (c) 17   (d) 99.

Chapter 19

Frequency Diagrams and Pie Charts

Pie charts

Pie charts are excellent for comparing figures. Each quantity is represented by a sector of a circle. As the angles at a point add up to 360°, this number figures a great deal.

EXAMPLES 1–2

1   60 customers were asked to name their favourite margarine. The results were as follows:

Fauna	11
Crane	13
Po-oc	16
Brass Band	20.

Draw a pie chart to illustrate this table.

Show your calculations: one customer is represented by $360 \div 60 = 6°$.

Fauna	$11 \times 6 = 66°$
Crane	$13 \times 6 = 78°$
Po-oc	$16 \times 6 = 96°$
Brass Band	$20 \times 6 = 120°.$

(Note: $66° + 78° + 96° + 120° = 360°$; a useful check.)

The pie chart can now be drawn. Label it carefully.

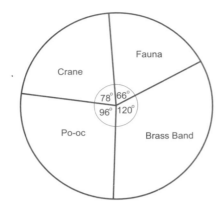

2   120 people were asked to choose in which of five countries they would like to spend their next summer holiday. This pie chart illustrates their answers:

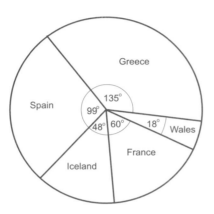

(a) Which country was most popular?   Clearly, Greece.
(b) Which country was least popular?   Wales, I'm afraid.
(c) How many people chose Spain?

Pie charts do not provide the actual figures easily. However, if 120 people are represented by 360°, one person is represented by 3°. So, the number of people choosing Spain was 99 ÷ 3 or 33.

Frequency diagrams

Bar charts look like this: Frequency polygons are like this:

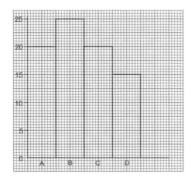   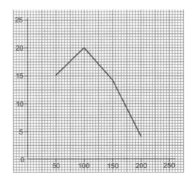

The examiner will ask you to do one of three things.

(1) Draw a bar chart.
(2) Draw a frequency polygon.
(3) Draw a frequency diagram.

If the examiner asks you to do the frequency diagram you can choose (1) or (2). On those occasions do not do both. If (1) **or** (2) is asked for, then do as you are told.

Bar charts

With these it is the correct heights that matter, although you must make sure that all your widths are the same. Often students make the last columns narrower as they are running out of space. This is a major clanger. You must start again! Otherwise you will lose marks.

AMPLE

3

Here is the same data used in the first pie chart.

Fauna	11
Crane	13
Po-oc	16
Brass Band	20

Here is the matching bar chart.

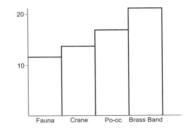

Frequency polygons

Again the widths must always be equal. Usually the data are in groups. The frequency is plotted above the middle of each group.

AMPLE

4

Here are the heights of 50 primary school children.

Class interval (cm)	f
120–125	0
125–130	7
130–135	15
135–140	20
140–145	8
145–150	0

Matching frequency polygon

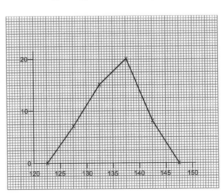

Two major errors are made by students:

(a) they fail to plot in the middle of every group;
(b) they do not study the vertical scales carefully.

Chapter 19

1   This pie chart illustrates the eye colour of 30 children in a class.

    (a) Use your pie chart to find:
        (i) the most common eye colour;
        (ii) the least common eye colour.
    (b) What angle represented one child?
    (c) How many children had green eyes?

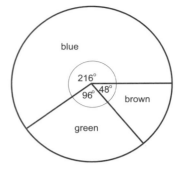

2   A student spent 24 h revising for G.C.S.E. mock examinations. The time was spent on four subjects in this way:

Mathematics	10 h
Science	8 h
History	5 h
French	1 h

    Draw a pie chart to illustrate this data.

3   80 boys ran 400 m. Here are their times in seconds:

Time	f
59.5–64.5	7
64.5–69.5	10
69.5–74.5	36
74.5–79.5	17
79.5–84.5	10

    Draw a frequency polygon to illustrate these figures.

4   The weights of 100 newborn babies are provided in the table below. Draw a bar chart to illustrate this data.

Weight (g)	f
2000–2500	6
2500–3000	19
3000–3500	38
3500–4000	28
4000–4500	9

5   The lives of 25 light bulbs were measured to the nearest hour. They were:

76	83	96	88	75
71	83	104	96	92
87	84	93	86	91
72	86	107	93	87
88	93	86	94	109

    Copy and complete this frequency distribution:

Life (nearest hour)	Tally	Freq. (*f*)
71–80	|||	4
81–90	‖‖‖ ‖‖‖	10
91–100		
101–110		
	Total	

Draw a frequency polygon to illustrate your frequency distribution.

Answers

ercise A   **1** (a)(i) blue, (ii) brown   (b) 12°   (c) 8
2 The angles were 150°, 120°, 75° and 15°.

Chapter 20

Probability

An introduction

If you throw a dice fairly, you would expect to get a four once in every six throws.
If you toss a coin, you would expect a head one time in every two attempts.
If you cut a pack of cards, you can expect to cut the ace of spades one time in 52.

These are statements of chance. In mathematics we use the word 'probability' instead of 'chance' and write our results as fractions:

the probability of a four was $\frac{1}{6}$
the probability of a head was $\frac{1}{2}$
the probability of the ace of spades was $\frac{1}{52}$.

This is often abbreviated to:

$$p(4) = \frac{1}{6}$$

$$p(\text{head}) = \frac{1}{2}$$

$$p(\text{ace of spades}) = \frac{1}{52}.$$

EXAMPLES

1–3

1   A bag contains ten beads: seven are black and three are red. If one is chosen at random, what is the probability of it being black?

There are seven black beads.
There are ten beads altogether.
$p(\text{black}) = \frac{7}{10}$.

2 A dice is rolled once. What is the probability of getting an even number?

There are three even numbers.
There are six numbers.
$p(\text{even}) = \frac{3}{6} = \frac{1}{2}$.

3 A pack of cards is shuffled. What is the probability that the top card is not a queen?

48 cards are not queens.
There are 52 cards.
$p(\text{not queen}) = \frac{48}{52} = \frac{12}{13}$.

Get into the habit of cancelling whenever it is possible. Now try the following exercise.

RCISE

A

1 A coin was tossed. What was the probability that it came down tails?

2 If you roll a dice, what is the probability that you obtain:
(a) a six?
(b) a multiple of three?
(c) a number which is not six?
(d) an odd number?

3 If you cut a pack of cards, what is the probability that:
(a) you get the king of spades?
(b) you get a black king?
(c) you do not get a king?
(d) you get a heart?

4 A jar contains 12 beads: six are red, four are green and two are yellow. If one of them is chosen at random, what is the probability that it is:
(a) red?
(b) green?
(c) yellow?
(d) not yellow?

Making lists

Occasionally the examiner will ask you to list all the possible outcomes when two events take place.

MPLES

4–5

4 Bill tossed a coin and rolled a dice. What are all the possible outcomes?

The secret is to have a system. Here is my solution. H is head and T is tails (of course). H1, H2, H3, H4, H5, H6. Notice that I did not alter H until I had run out of numbers. Then T1, T2, T3, T4, T5 and T6. There were 12 ($2 \times 6 = 12$).

5   Every Saturday Mary plays football and Brian plays hockey. Complete this list of possible results. M is Mary, B is Brian, W = wins, D = draws and L = loses.
(1) BW MW ....

I will stick to Brian winning at first so (2) BW MD (3) BW ML. I have to change.
(4) BD MW (5) BD MD (6) BD ML. Now switch to BL.
(7) BL MW (8) BL MD (9) BL ML.
There were 9 (3 ×3 = 9).

EXERCISE

B

1   Tom wants to paint two different coloured stripes on his car's roof. He has red, green, yellow and blue paints. Make a list of the various pairs he can choose from.

2   A newsagent employs three boys. He keeps a record of whether they are on time or not. He keeps his records like this: o = on time, l = late.

	Alan	Brian	Chris
All on time is	o	o	o

Make a full list of the other possibilities.

Repeated events

When an event is repeated, a diagram is often used to find probabilities. It is called a *tree diagram*.

EXAMPLES

6–7

6   A coin is tossed twice. What is the probability that it comes down tails both times?

$$p(\text{H}) = \tfrac{1}{2} \qquad p(\text{T}) = \tfrac{1}{2}$$

The lowest branches lead to two tails.
You multiply the fractions on each branch.
Therefore $p(\text{both tails}) = \tfrac{1}{2} \times \tfrac{1}{2} = \tfrac{1}{4}$.

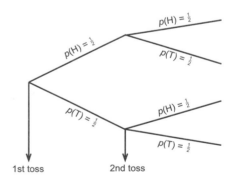

7   A dice is rolled twice. Use a tree diagram to find the probability that a 6 is scored on both occasions.

The lowest branch gives two sixes.
$p(\text{both } 6) = \tfrac{1}{6} \times \tfrac{1}{6} = \tfrac{1}{36}$.

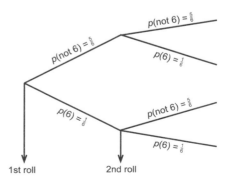

1   This spinner was spun twice. Use a tree diagram to find the probability that a score of 2 was obtained each time.

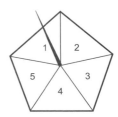

2   A bag contained two red balls and one black ball. A ball was selected; its colour was noted and it was returned to the bag. The event was repeated. Use a tree diagram to find the probability that the ball was red on both occasions.

3   A pack of cards was cut and the suit of the top card recorded. The event was repeated. This tree diagram shows the probability of cutting hearts.

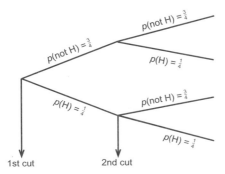

Use this diagram to find the probability that:

You cut a heart: (a)   on both occasions
                   (b)   on neither occasion.

Two events

Sometimes we need to find the probability that two quite different events both happen. The method always involves multiplying. Tree diagrams can again be used to display the working.

8   The probability that Gareth wins at squash is $\frac{3}{10}$.
    The probability that Hywel will win his pool match is $\frac{3}{4}$.

   (a) Draw a tree diagram to show all the possible results.
   (b) Use the tree diagram to find that probability that
       (i)   they both win
       (ii) they both lose
       (iii) only one of them wins

First you must realise that the 'losing probabilities' are $\frac{7}{10}$ and $\frac{1}{4}$. The tree diagram will look like this.

(i) $p(\text{both win}) = \dfrac{3}{10} \times \dfrac{3}{4} = \dfrac{9}{40}.$

(ii) $p(\text{both lose}) = \dfrac{7}{10} \times \dfrac{1}{4} = \dfrac{7}{40}.$

(iii) This is two questions in one.
Perhaps only Gareth will win.
Perhaps only Hywel.

$$p(\text{Gareth only}) = \dfrac{3}{10} \times \dfrac{1}{4} = \dfrac{3}{40}.$$

$$p(\text{Hywel only}) = \dfrac{7}{10} \times \dfrac{3}{4} = \dfrac{21}{40}.$$

So the probability of either of these is $\dfrac{3}{40} + \dfrac{21}{40} = \dfrac{3}{5}$ (fraction key used).

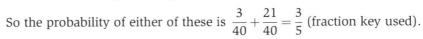

9   The probability that Manchester Utd will win the Premier League is $\frac{2}{5}$. The probability that Swindon will win Division 1 is $\frac{3}{20}$. This tree diagram represents the four possibilities.

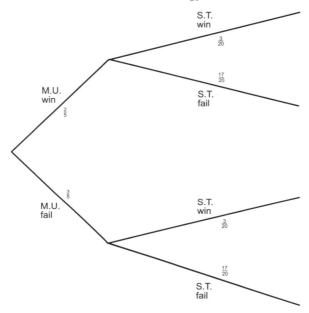

Use this tree diagram to find the probability that only one of these teams is successful.

Again this is two questions in one. It may be that only Manchester Utd is successful, but it could be the outsiders Swindon Town.

$$p(\text{Manchester Utd only}) = \dfrac{2}{5} \times \dfrac{17}{20} = \dfrac{17}{50}. \qquad p(\text{Swindon Town only}) = \dfrac{3}{5} \times \dfrac{3}{20} = \dfrac{9}{100}.$$

Therefore the probability of either is $\dfrac{17}{50} + \dfrac{9}{100} = \dfrac{43}{100}.$

EXERCISE

D

1   Tomorrow the probability that it will rain is $\frac{1}{5}$ and the probability that Tim will get no mail is $\frac{1}{6}$. Draw a tree diagram to show the four possible outcomes. Use the diagram to find the probability that (a) it rains and Tim gets no mail and (b) it is fine all day and he gets at least one letter.

2 The probability that the favourite will win the Derby this year is $\frac{3}{7}$. The probability that an Englishman will win Wimbledon in the next 10 years is $\frac{1}{4}$. Again, draw a tree diagram to show the four possibilities. Use it to find the probability that only one of these events happens.

This is a major topic in the intermediate course. Be sure you are at ease with the contents of this exercise.

1 A dice is rolled. Find the probability that the score is (a) a 3, (b) not a 3, (c) even.

2 A jar contains two black beads, three yellow beads and one white bead. One bead is chosen at random; find the probability that its colour is (a) black, (b) not black, (c) black or yellow, (d) red.

3 At a certain crossroads the probability that the traffic lights are red is $\frac{7}{10}$.
(a) What is the probability that the lights are not red?
A motorist approaches these lights on two consecutive days. Draw a tree diagram to illustrate the four possible outcomes. Use your diagram to find the probability that (b) the lights are red both times, (c) the lights are not red either time.

4 The probability that Kate will pass her Mathematics test is $\frac{7}{10}$. The probability that Liz passes in English is $\frac{5}{6}$. Calculate the probability that only one of them passes. You are advised to draw a tree diagram.

Answers

ercise **A**   **1** $\frac{1}{2}$ **2** (a) $\frac{1}{6}$, (b) $\frac{1}{3}$, (c) $\frac{5}{6}$, (d) $\frac{1}{2}$ **3** (a) $\frac{1}{52}$, (b) $\frac{1}{26}$, (c) $\frac{12}{13}$, (d) $\frac{1}{4}$ **4** (a) $\frac{1}{2}$, (b) $\frac{1}{3}$, (c) $\frac{1}{6}$, (d) $\frac{5}{6}$.

ercise **B**   **1** RG, RY, RB, GY, GB and YB
2 ooo, ool, olo, oll, loo, lol, llo and lll.

ercise **C**   **1** $\frac{1}{25}$ **2** $\frac{4}{9}$ **3** (a) $\frac{1}{16}$, (b) $\frac{9}{16}$.

ercise **D**   **1** (a) $\frac{1}{30}$, (b) $\frac{2}{3}$ **2** $\frac{13}{28}$ $\left(\frac{9}{28} + \frac{1}{7}\right)$.

ercise **E**   **1** (a) $\frac{1}{6}$, (b) $\frac{5}{6}$, (c) $\frac{1}{2}$ **2** (a) $\frac{1}{3}$, (b) $\frac{2}{3}$, (c) $\frac{5}{6}$, (d) 0   **3** (a) $\frac{3}{10}$, (b) $\frac{49}{100}$, (c) $\frac{9}{100}$ **4** $\frac{11}{30}$.

Chapter 21

Scatter Diagrams

EXAMPLES

1–2

It does seem likely that there is a link between a child's age and a child's ability to read. In mathematics we call the connection between two sets of figures the *correlation*.

1   Eight children of various ages were given a word recognition test at the primary school. Here are their results with their ages:

Age in months	60	73	83	97	109	120	128	130
No. of words read	10	25	43	65	73	93	110	114

The graph below has been plotted with ages horizontal and words vertical. A suitable scale was chosen. As you can see, the points nearly formed a straight line. The line which has been drawn is called the 'line of best fit'. It is done by eye.

This is a good example of *positive* correlation. *Older* children read *more* words in this case. This type of graph is called a 'scatter diagram'.

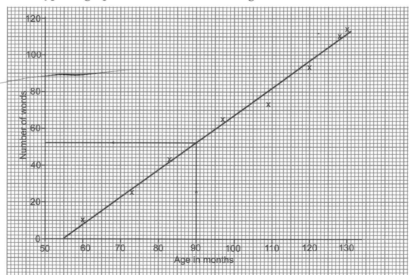

The line can be used to make some estimates, e.g. we would expect a child aged 90 months to be able to read 52 words. Notice how the method of obtaining this estimate is marked clearly on the graph. This is good examination practice.

2   The table below contains information about six teams from the football league.

	A	B	C	D	E	F
No. of goals against	87	80	65	55	45	30
No. of matches won	5	12	15	20	22	30

It does seem likely that there will be some correlation. A scatter diagram might show this.

The scatter diagram below shows *negative* correlation. In other words, if you let your opponents score lots of goals then, at the end of the day, you don't win matches.

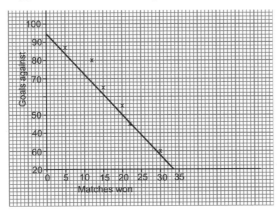

Types of scatter diagram

Scatter diagrams usually fall into five types in examinations. Rough sketches with suitable comments follow. These comments are sometimes requested.

Excellent positive correlation

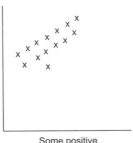

Some positive correlation

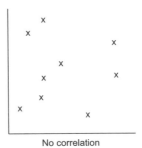

No correlation

Excellent negative correlation

Some negative correlation

EXERCISE

A

1   (a)   (b)   (c)   (d)

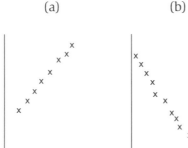  

Comment on the type of correlation illustrated in each of the scatter diagrams above.

2   Match these axes to the scatter diagrams in question 1:

	x-axis	*y*-axis
(a)	a boy's age	his height
(b)	seats occupied in a bus	seats empty
(c)	temperature in °C	temperature in °F
(d)	a girl's age	the number on her front door.

3   The table below contains the weights to the nearest kilogram and the heights to the nearest centimetre of ten girls in a comprehensive school.

Weight (kg)	37	40	43	44	48	53	56	60	61	63
Height (cm)	134	139	144	156	151	154	158	160	167	171

Plot a scatter diagram.

    Let 2 cm = 5 kg on the vertical axis (start at 30 kg).
    Let 2 cm = 5 cm on the horizontal axis (start at 130 cm).

Draw the line of best fit. Comment on the type of correlation. Use your line to:

(a) estimate the height of a girl of weight 44 kg;

(b) estimate the weight of a girl whose height is 164 cm.

4   The following information is known about a certain country:

Year:	1945	1948	1951	1954	1957	1960
No. of T.V.s owned per 1000 population	6	110	190	250	308	400
Cinema visits monthly per 1000 population	400	334	275	230	200	134

(a) Plot a scatter diagram. Use a scale of 1 cm = 20 'T.V.s' vertically, and 1 cm = 40 'visits' horizontally.

(b) Draw a line of best fit.

(c) Comment on the nature of the correlation.

(d) In 1952, 210 T.V.s per 1000 population were owned. *Use your line* to estimate the number of cinema visits made per 1000.

5   The table below shows the examination results in Mathematics and Physics of nine students. The maximum mark in each was 100.

Mathematics	16	24	37	48	52	60	68	77	80
Physics	30	38	44	55	59	69	71	82	80

(a) Plot a scatter diagram.

(b) Comment on the type of correlation.

(c) Draw a line of best fit.

(d) Two students missed an examination each. '*A*' scored 57 in Maths, and '*B*' scored 57 in Physics. Use your line to estimate what *A* would have scored in Physics and what *B* would have scored in Mathematics.

Answers

Exercise A

1 (a) Excellent positive correlation   (b) excellent negative correlation
   (c) some positive correlation   (d) no correlation.

2 (a) Diagram c   (b) diagram b   (c) diagram a   (d) diagram d.

3 Some positive correlation   (a) about 145 cm   (b) about 59 kg.

4 (c) Some negative correlation   (d) about 260.

5 (b) You should have a good positive correlation   (d) *A* 62,   *B* 50.

Chapter 22

The Mean, Median and Mode, Including Cumulative Frequency Curves

Essential Skills

The careful use of your calculator.

(a) Σf means the total of the f column.

(b) $\Sigma(n \times f)$ means the total of the $n \times f$ column.

Basic Facts

The mean, median and mode are all measures of the *middle*.

The mean of a series of numbers is found by adding them and dividing the total by the number of numbers.

The median is found by writing them in ascending order and picking the middle one.

The mode is the number in a series which occurs most often.

The range is the simplest measure of spread.

Cumulative frequency curves are sometimes needed to estimate the median, the quartiles, and the interquartile range.

EXAMPLES

1–5

1 Find the mean, the median, the mode and the range of: 7, 8, 9, 6, 6, 6, 5 and 9.

The mean $= \frac{1}{8}(7 + 8 + 9 + 6 + 6 + 6 + 5 + 9)$
$= \frac{56}{8} = 7.$

To find the median, write the numbers in order and identify the middle one.
In order, the numbers are 5, 6, 6, 6, 7, 8, 9, 9.
As there is an even number of numbers in the series, there are two middle numbers. The mean of these two numbers is taken as the median, i.e.

$$\frac{6+7}{2} = 6.5.$$

The mode is 6, as there are more sixes than any other number.

The range is the difference between the smallest and largest, so:
the range $= 9 - 5 = 4.$

2 When there are a large number of numbers, the information is provided in the form of a frequency distribution or table. Here are 25 numbers.

3	3	3	4	4
4	4	4	5	5
5	5	5	5	5
5	6	6	6	6
7	7	7	8	8

They could be represented in a table like this:

Number (n)	Frequency (f)	$n \times f$
3	3	9
4	5	20
5	8	40
6	4	24
7	3	21
8	2	16
Total	**25**	**130**

The sum of the f column (written Σf) is clearly 25. The column $n \times f$ was introduced to speed the addition of 25 numbers.

The mean $= \dfrac{130}{25}$ or $\dfrac{\Sigma(n \times f)}{\Sigma f} = 5.2$.

The median (the 13th number) is 5 (by inspection).

The mode is 5.

The range is $8 - 3 = 5$.

Mean problems are occasionally asked in reverse. The key word here is *totals*.
The total = mean × the number of numbers.

3 The mean of four numbers is 25. The numbers are 17, 23, 29 and x. Find x.

The total of the four numbers is $25 \times 4 = 100$.
The total of the three numbers we know is 69.
The fourth number must be $100 - 69 = 31$.

4 The mean of six numbers is 45. Find their total.

The total is $6 \times 45 = 270$.

5 Present the following 30 numbers in a frequency table. Use this table to calculate the mean and to find the median and the mode.

7	11	9	8	7	8
11	8	7	6	8	7
5	8	9	8	5	9
8	6	8	7	8	4
10	6	8	10	8	8

The table is usually prepared by using a tally.

Number n	Tally	Freq. f	$n \times f$
4	|	1	4
5	||	2	10
6	|||	3	18
7	⌿⌿⌿⌿	5	35
8	⌿⌿⌿⌿ ⌿⌿⌿⌿ ||	12	96
9	|||	3	27
10	||	2	20
11	||	2	22
Total		**30**	**232**

The total Σf must be 30. (If yours isn't then you made a mistake. Check your tally and totals again.) Estimate the answer. It must be in the region of 7, because the numbers range from 4 to 11.

$$\text{Mean} = \frac{\Sigma(n \times f)}{\Sigma f} = \frac{232}{30} = 7\frac{11}{15} = 7.73 \quad (2 \text{ d.p.}).$$

By inspection, the middle numbers (15th and 16th) are both 8; the number occurring most frequently is also 8. So, the median is 8 and the mode is 8.

EXERCISE

A

Try these questions.

1 Find the mean, median, mode and range of: 21, 16, 14, 13, 14, 17 and 20.

2 Find the mean, median, mode and range of the following numbers:

N	f
6	7
7	14
8	12
9	10
10	7

3 The mean of five numbers is 20. The mean of the four smallest is 15. Find the largest number.

Cumulative frequency curves

Consider these seven numbers: 8, 11, 13, 17, 19, 23, 24.

(a) What is the median?
(b) What is the third smallest?
(c) What is the second largest?

(a) 17 (middle one)   (b) 13   (c) 23 of course.

If the data are presented in groups the work is no longer simple.

AMPLE

6

6   200 motorists were asked to record the number of miles they travelled in a particular week. The results were:

Distance	f
1–50	17
51–100	38
101–150	40
151–200	66
201–250	27
251–300	12

Estimate:

(a) the median
(b) the number of cars covering less than 80 miles
(c) the number of cars exceeding 174 miles.

A cumulative frequency table is needed. It looks like this:

Distance	Cumulative frequency	
50 or less	17	as before
100 or less	55	(17 + 38)
150 or less	95	(55 + 40)
200 or less	161	(95 + 66)
250 or less	188	(161 + 27)
300 or less	200	(188 + 12)

Now a cumulative frequency curve must be drawn.

There are many places to go wrong when tackling this level 8 skill.

(i)   You must plot at the *end of each group*.
      50 or less   17   is plotted at (50, 17)
      100 or less   55   is plotted at (100, 55).

(ii) Join the points with a smooth curve; the curve will increase steadily. *It cannot decrease.*
(iii) Close the curve to the origin, although (0, 0) is not on your table.

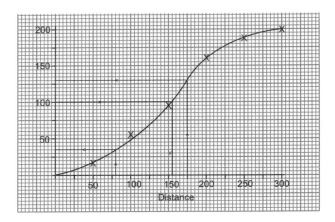

(a) The median is 155 miles
(b) 35 cars
(c) 200 − 130 = 70 cars.   Again, these recordings are marked clearly on the curve.

Sometimes, two other readings are requested. They are:

(a) the lower quartile;
(b) the upper quartile.

They are the $\frac{1}{4}$ and $\frac{3}{4}$ points on the cumulative frequency. The following graph illustrates this.

These are the exam marks of 400 children (maximum 200).
The lower quartile is 85. Read at 100 ($\frac{1}{4}$ of 400)
The upper quartile is 130. Read at 300 ($\frac{3}{4}$ of 400).

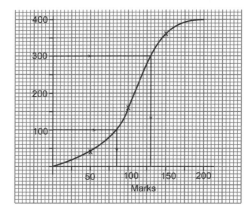

A useful measure of spread known as the *interquartile range* is a popular question. It is simply upper quartile − lower quartile. In this case it is 130 − 85 = 45.

Chapter 22

7   The amount of pocket money received by 160 Year 8 pupils is recorded below in groups.

£0.00–£1	17
£1.01–£2	31
£2.01–£3	52
£3.01–£4	45
£4.01–£5	15

(a) Complete a cumulative frequency table.

(b) Draw a cumulative frequency curve.

Use your curve to estimate:

(c) the median amount of pocket money;

(d) the interquartile range of the amounts of pocket money.

The table is:

£1 or less	17
£2 or less	48
£3 or less	100
£4 or less	145
£5 or less	160

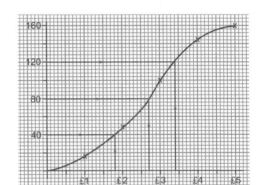

The median amount is £2.70.

The interquartile range is £3.40 − £1.80 = £1.60.

Now tackle these exercises.

1   200 pupils sat an intermediate G.C.S.E. English examination. The results are recorded below in groups.

Group	f
0–20	18
21–40	33
41–60	62
61–80	40
81–100	30
101–120	17

(a) Complete a cumulative frequency table.

(b) Draw a cumulative frequency curve.

Use your curve to estimate:

(c) (i) the median mark

(ii) the interquartile range of these marks.

2 In a fishing competition 120 fish were caught. The table below presents their weight in grams.

Weight	f
0–500	7
500–1000	16
1000–1500	23
1500–2000	40
2000–2500	20
2500–3000	14

(a) Compile a cumulative frequency table.

(b) Draw a cumulative frequency curve.

Use your curve to find:

(c) (i) the interquartile range;

    (ii) the number of fish weighing less than 1400 g;

    (iii) the number of fish weighing more than 1850 g.

Answers

Exercise A

1 mean $= 16.4$ median $= 16$ mode $= 14$ range $= 8$

2 mean $= 7.92$ median $= 8$ mode $= 7$ range $= 4$

3 40.

Exercise B

These part (c) answers are approximate.

1 (c)(i) 56   (ii) $79 - 39 = 40$

2 (c)(i) 900 g   (ii) 41   (iii) 46.